PENGUI
THE

Navtej Sarna was born in Jalandhur, ... After studying Law at Delhi University, he joined the Indian Foreign Service in 1980. He has served as a diplomat in Moscow, Geneva, Tehran and Washington DC, and as India's Foreign Office Spokesman in New Delhi. He is currently India's ambassador to Israel.

His first novel, *We Weren't Lovers Like That*, was published in 2003 and has been translated into Arabic and Hindi. He is also the author of two non-fiction works, *The Book of Nanak* and *Folk Tales of Poland*. His short stories have been broadcast over the BBC World Service and published in India and UK. He contributes regularly to the *Times Literary Supplement*, the *Hindu* and other journals.

to his immense credit, captures the sights, sounds and smells of each of these places perfectly. The minutest detail is well captured in the book, a result of some painstaking research undertaken by Sarna ... A better story on the Punjab's first family could not have been told'—*Business Standard*.

'A deeply moving and gripping story. *The Exile* traces the emotional and spiritual exile rather than the mere geographical exile of the Maharaja'—*Mail Today*

'The novelist scores on two important points: the first, [Navtej Sarna] captures the climate of intrigue that prevailed after Ranjit Singh's death, and second, Duleep Singh's own confusion, humiliation, and pathos growing up in a world of betrayal and continuous political turmoil and his vain but sincere effort to come good. The "Rashomon-like" multiple narrative technique is necessary here, because very little is known about Duleep Singh's mind, though there is a reasonable amount of information available on his daily life as an adult in England ... Kudos to Navtej Sarna for telling such a moving story'—*The Hindu*

'The overwhelming sense of the novel is of a world that was lost; a world governed by honour and valour as much as chicanery and intrigue. The descriptions of the struggle for power after Ranjit Singh's death are marvelous in summoning up a time when integrity clashed with opportunism and braggadocio with statesmanship'—*DNA*

'The details and the narrative that emerge are rich and make good reading because of the five pairs of eyes that take you through the tragedy of Punjab as it splintered after Ranjit Singh's death. Even the account of the maidservant, the charming and ambitious Mangla, details an important segment of Indian life in the 19th century. It is almost Manto-esque, with descriptions of Lahore, Hira Mandi, the punkahwallahs, the kanjarkhana, and the deep desire of a girl there to escape the gullies and bazaars and make it to higher quarters. *The Exile* deals with much more than just the estrangement of a failed prince from Punjab, who found both his father's legacy and the hostile circumstances unbearable'—*The Indian Express*

'There are nuanced descriptions of life in the harems of Lahore that are fascinating and rich. Sarna's grasp of the language is assured and his feelings for the cause are strong ... [Sarna] puts Duleep Singh's cause forward compellingly and his work is undoubtedly soundly researched'—*The Statesman*

'A sensitive exploration of the pangs of exile, the novel is rich in poignant moments'—*Hindustan Times*

'Extremely moving'—*Asian Age*

THE EXILE

A Novel Based on the Life of
Maharaja Duleep Singh

Navtej Sarna

PENGUIN BOOKS
Published by the Penguin Group
Penguin Books India Pvt. Ltd, 11 Community Centre, Panchsheel Park, New Delhi 110 017, India
Penguin Group (USA) Inc., 375 Hudson Street, New York, New York 10014, USA
Penguin Group (Canada), 90 Eglinton Avenue East, Suite 700, Toronto, Ontario, M4P 2Y3, Canada (a division of Pearson Penguin Canada Inc.)
Penguin Books Ltd, 80 Strand, London WC2R 0RL, England
Penguin Ireland, 25 St Stephen's Green, Dublin 2, Ireland (a division of Penguin Books Ltd)
Penguin Group (Australia), 250 Camberwell Road, Camberwell, Victoria 3124, Australia (a division of Pearson Australia Group Pty Ltd)
Penguin Group (NZ), 67 Apollo Drive, Rosedale, North Shore 0632, New Zealand (a division of Pearson New Zealand Ltd)
Penguin Group (South Africa) (Pty) Ltd, 24 Sturdee Avenue, Rosebank, Johannesburg 2196, South Africa

Penguin Books Ltd, Registered Offices: 80 Strand, London WC2R 0RL, England

First published in Viking by Penguin Books India 2008
Published in Penguin Books 2010

Copyright © Navtej Sarna 2008

All rights reserved

10 9 8 7 6 5 4 3 2 1

ISBN 9780143068822

Typeset in Minion Regular by SÜRYA, New Delhi
Printed at Gopsons Papers Ltd, Noida

To all those who died in exile

Exile is strangely compelling to think about but terrible to experience. It is the unhealable rift forced between a human being and a native place, between the self and its true home: its essential sadness can never be surmounted. And while it is true that literature and history contain heroic, romantic, glorious, even triumphant episodes in an exile's life, these are no more than efforts meant to overcome the crippling sorrow of estrangement. The achievements of exile are permanently undermined by the loss of something left behind forever.

—*Edward Said*, Reflections on Exile

CONTENTS

AUTHOR'S NOTE

It was nearly forty years ago that I first heard mention, in tragic terms, of Maharaja Duleep Singh from my mother. Since then, his name has always evoked a predominant feeling of poignancy. A child duped of his kingdom, a man who changed his religion twice, a king who yearned to come back to his people but never could—his story seemed to hold an unusually high emotional quotient, which could never quite be communicated by the cold bare-bones approach of history, weighed down as it is by the bias of those who are in a position to write it. Moreover, the Maharaja's complex personality, acquiescent then rebellious, fractured by a lack of belonging, embittered by persistent injustice, became an easy target of dismissive and patronizing comment. Whatever his faults, it seemed to me, he deserved better. Most available histories of the time have not done justice to all his aspects as a human being. What, for instance, did he feel? What did he think?

If one had to reach for the edges of Duleep Singh's story then the answer, to my mind, lay in pushing available facts towards the realm of fiction, but pushing them gently, so as not to distort them. The documents, files, letters, memoranda, recollections needed to be turned into a fictional narrative that would fill the gaps left by history. This book is the result of that attempt, however imperfect. It is ultimately a novel, but a novel that has tried to be true to history: thanks to meticulous documentation, all the major events of the Maharaja's life, the dates, the addresses, the journeys, even the list of precious items taken away from his treasury, or toshakhana, can be substantiated in fact.

I owe a debt of gratitude to much that has been written before. Sitaram Kohli's *Sunset of the Sikh Empire*, Khushwant Singh's *A*

History of the Sikhs, Sohan Lal Suri's *Umdat-i-Tawarik* and P.K. Nijhawan's *The First Punjab War* helped immensely to understand the tumultuous years before the annexation of Punjab. *Lady Login's Recollections*, Dr Ganda Singh's *Maharaja Duleep Singh Correspondence*, Michael Alexander and Sushila Anand's *Queen Victoria's Maharaja*, Christy Campbell's *The Maharaja's Box* and Peter Bance's *The Duleep Singhs* were instrumental in constructing the Maharaja's later life. I have relied on much else—memoirs of British soldiers, nineteenth-century tourist literature, letters, files as well as personal visits to Lahore, Elveden, Moscow and Paris. For access to many out-of-print books I thank Mary Yarnell of the Library of Congress, Washington, DC. My thanks, too, to the National Archives in New Delhi for access to several valuable files, including the relatively unused material on Duleep Singh's days in Fattehgarh and Mussoorie.

My friend and editor at Penguin India, Ravi Singh, has contributed, over several years, far more to this novel than he would care to admit, constantly guiding my enthusiasm in the right direction. To him I am immensely grateful.

A very special word of thanks to my family—Avina, Satyajit and Nooreen—for living indulgently and affectionately with this obsession for nearly a decade. And to my mother, Surjit, for starting me on this trail and my late father, Mohinder Singh Sarna, for kindling in me a love for Sikh history through his own epic poetry.

And ultimately, thanks to that Island of the soul without which this book may not have been completed, an Island where there is peace and writing can be a waking dream.

CAST OF CHARACTERS

THE NARRATORS

Maharaja Duleep Singh: The youngest of the acknowledged sons of the legendary Maharaja Ranjit Singh, he came to the throne of Punjab at the age of five, in the wake of bloodshed and chaos after Ranjit Singh's death.

Mangla: The favourite slave girl of Duleep's mother, Maharani Jindan, Mangla wielded considerable political influence at the Lahore court during the years when the child Duleep was king.

Dr John Login: A Presbyterian surgeon in the Bengal army, he was appointed by Lord Dalhousie as the Superintendent of Duleep Singh after the annexation of Punjab.

Lady Lena Login: Dr Login's wife who, along with her husband, had a strong influence on the child Duleep in India and during his early years in England.

Arur Singh: Duleep's faithful servant of many years, he was a close companion of the Maharaja during the years of his rebellion in Paris and Moscow.

General Charles Carrol-Tevis: An American soldier of fortune, Carrol-Tevis became a confidant of Duleep Singh in Paris.

AND OTHERS

Maharani Jind Kaur or Jindan: Daughter of the royal kennel keeper, she was one of Ranjit Singh's later queens and mother of Duleep Singh.

Maharaja Kharak Singh: The eldest son of Ranjit Singh from Maharani Raj Kaur. He came to the throne on the old king's death.

Maharaja Sher Singh: Ranjit Singh's acknowledged son from his first queen Mehtab Kaur.

Kanwars Multana Singh, Peshaura Singh, Kashmira Singh, Tara Singh: Other acknowledged sons of Ranjit Singh.

Kanwar Naunihal Singh: Son of Kharak Singh. A smart and astute soldier, he was a favourite of Maharaja Ranjit Singh.

The Dogra brothers: The three Dogra brothers joined the service of Maharaja Ranjit Singh as troopers and rapidly rose to great eminence and influence in the Lahore court:

> **Gulab Singh**—a skilful general and astute politician, he ended up as ruler of Jammu and Kashmir;
>
> **Dhian Singh**—rose to become Ranjit Singh's powerful Prime Minister or Wazir;
>
> **Suchet Singh**—the youngest brother, was a polished courtier and a gallant soldier.

Hira Singh: Son of Dhian Singh and a favourite of Maharaja Ranjit Singh. He was appointed Wazir during Duleep's infancy.

Pandit Jalla: A close adviser of Hira Singh.

The Sandhawalia Sardars: Sikh chiefs **Attar Singh** and **Lehna Singh** and their nephew **Ajit Singh**. They were related to Maharaja Ranjit Singh and played a critical role in his campaigns and during the battles for the throne after his death. **Thaker Singh Sandhawalia** was their descendant.

The Attariwala Sardars: Sham Singh, a legendary hero who died in the battle of Sabraon; his brother **Chatar Singh**, who together with his son **Sher Singh** fought the British in the second Anglo-Sikh war.

Fakir Nuruddin, Zehuruddin, Dewan Deena Nath: Ministers and senior courtiers in the Lahore court.

Bamba Muller: Duleep Singh's first wife.

Victor, Frederick, Bamba, Catherine, Sophia and **Albert:** Duleep Singh's children from Bamba.

Ada Douglas Wetherill: Duleep Singh's second wife.

Pauline and **Irene:** Duleep Singh's daughters from Ada.

Lord Dalhousie: Governor General of India, 1848–56.

IMPORTANT DATES

13 November 1780	Birth of Ranjit Singh
4 September 1838	Birth of Duleep Singh
27 June 1839	Death of Ranjit Singh Kharak Singh proclaimed Maharaja
5 November 1840	Deaths of Kharak Singh and Naunihal Singh
18 January 1841	Sher Singh proclaimed Maharaja
15 September 1843	Deaths of Sher Singh and Dhian Singh Duleep Singh proclaimed Maharaja
13 December 1845	Declaration of war by the British
9 March 1846	First Treaty of Lahore
16 December 1846	Treaty of Bhyrowal
29 March 1849	Second Treaty of Lahore, Annexation of Punjab
February 1850	Removal of Duleep Singh to Fattehgarh
8 March 1853	Baptism of Duleep Singh as a Christian
19 April 1854	Departure of Duleep Singh for England
1 August 1863	Death of Maharani Jindan
18 October 1863	Death of John Login
7 June 1864	Marriage of Duleep Singh with Bamba
25 May 1886	Baptism of Duleep Singh again as a Sikh
20 May 1889	Marriage of Duleep Singh with Ada
22 October 1893	Death of Duleep Singh

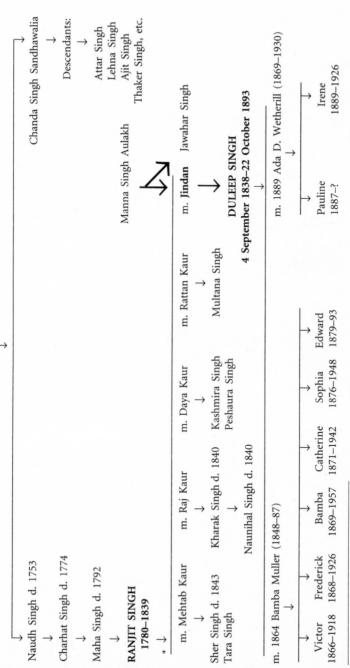

Budh Singh d. 1716

Naudh Singh d. 1753

Charhat Singh d. 1774

Maha Singh d. 1792

RANJIT SINGH
1780–1839

Chanda Singh Sandhawalia

Descendants:

Attar Singh
Lehna Singh
Ajit Singh
Thaker Singh, etc.

Manna Singh Aulakh

m. Mehtab Kaur   m. Raj Kaur   m. Daya Kaur   m. Rattan Kaur   m. **Jindan**   Jawahar Singh

Sher Singh d. 1843   Kharak Singh d. 1840   Kashmira Singh   Multana Singh   **DULEEP SINGH**
Tara Singh   Peshaura Singh   **4 September 1838–22 October 1893**

                        Naunihal Singh d. 1840

m. 1864 Bamba Muller (1848–87)   m. 1889 Ada D. Wetherill (1869–1930)

Victor   Frederick   Bamba   Catherine   Sophia   Edward   Pauline   Irene
1866–1918   1868–1926   1869–1957 1871–1942   1876–1948   1879–93   1887–?   1889–1926

*Only those of Ranjit Singh's queens whose sons were acknowledged as his have been shown

PROLOGUE

On winter nights, when the moon rides into a dagger-sharp sky on her chariot of two wispy clouds, our Punjab looks very beautiful, like it has never been wounded, never divided and broken up. The five rivers twisting towards the great Indus, like dark serpents swollen with the blood of centuries, belong to one people. And on all our villages, our thousands of ancient villages, fall gently, like the moonlight, the blessings of all the gods.

On such nights, the azan, the mantra and the kirtan all make the same music. And to this music, if you look for them as your own, you will find the dervish dancing in the village square and Sohni humming for her Mahiwal on the banks of the Chenab.

And the past is close at hand. The low Siwalik hills echo the hooves of the plundering armies of Ghazni and Nadir Shah. There is the din of so many battles, the sound of sword on shield, the trumpeting of elephants, the booming of cannon. Grandmothers warming their bones by the chullah and peasants sitting around winter bonfires, wrapped up in rough blankets against the frost—these guardians of memory, they tell stories. Of Gobind Singh's battles against the Mughals, of Banda Bahadur's terrible revenge on Sirhind, of the Sikhs living in jungles, each man's head priced at fifty rupees, harrying retreating Afghan armies.

They talk longest about a lion-hearted boy of twelve—Ranjit Singh Sukerchekia, who united Punjab under one banner, and soon became the most powerful Maharaja in Hindustan. From the Sutlej to the Khyber, all on which his one-eyed gaze fell became his.

They talk also of the terrible years that followed his death, the bloodletting, the betrayals, the coming of the British.

And sometimes, they talk of the lionheart's son Duleep, the last Maharaja of our Punjab.

Book One

THE DYING LIGHT

Duleep Singh, autumn 1893, Paris

Does it matter where one dies, in which country, which land? Does it matter at all if the last breath is drawn among your own people, friends and lovers, or among strangers, or completely alone? If you have not lived at home, perhaps there is no cause to die there.

And what is home? Where I was born, or where I lived all my life? Do I call Punjab my home, or England? If I had a choice, where would I want my bones to become dust, and would it matter?

I know these things mattered to my mother. Bibiji. Beautiful Jindan, ruined by the same fate as I—at this hour I will even admit that perhaps we were both small and inadequate and the times demanded too much of us ... But no—a dying mind wanders. When I met my mother in Calcutta, after our separation of fourteen years, before she decided to come with me to England, her only wish was to pass her remaining days at some holy place on the banks of the Ganges. She would never have been at peace if I had let her bones lie in England, far away from the land of her ancestors. That is why I had to do what I did, carry her back across the seas, let the few fistfuls of her burnt-out remains flow into the Godavari. I could not immerse her ashes in the Ganges or the Sutlej but at least she was in India. I remember how the waters churned the ashes, curled around them, swept them away. And even as I watched, a swift current took hold of them and soon it all became the same, the water and my mother only a sheet of twilight silver, vanishing fast.

I remember that moment, though I have forgotten much else. My memory is almost gone; this stroke has finished me. I can barely move. Stretching out for that glass of water on the table seems the most difficult of things. And that light, the patch of sky I see from the window, grows fainter by the day. A curtain is being drawn across everything and I no longer have the will, or even the desire, to fight. It is true that I am dying.

But there are days when, if I shut my eyes, strange colours can still rise in my mind, forgotten words, songs, faces, and the lost caress of the breezes of Lahore. Sometimes, when the light is of a particular shade, especially on late winter afternoons, I see myself in the Lahore fort . . . I am standing at one of the arched windows of my mother's haveli, above a four-quartered garden with its marble fountain and walkways paved with thin bricks. Beyond the cypress trees I see a marble pavilion and still beyond, past the wall of the fort, the plain stretching away to the ribbon of water that is the Ravi. Somewhere there, I used to imagine, were all the battles fought between the Sikhs in blazing yellow and the British in red. I can hear the elephants swaying up the broad marble staircase that came up right under the Summan Burj. I was scared the first time I sat in a silver howdah and came up that staircase; I held on tight to the silver railing in front of me. I don't remember who was with me then. Not Bibiji, else I would not have been afraid.

And there is the memory of the light filtering through the filigree of marble on to the floor of the haveli, making patterns that I would step on and imagine myself dressed in a gown woven with light. I wondered then how the light came to us from so far away, how the sun rose and set. I'd asked Mangla once, and she had said, 'Ask the Angrez and he'll tell you his race controls it all.' Or perhaps this never happened, perhaps it is only a false memory and I imagine this because the British certainly were to control all my days and nights, all my stars. My life, such as it was.

I see my mother's chamber often these days, sometimes even with my eyes open. The mind, I have heard, has a way of helping the body cope with physical suffering, and perhaps that is why I see that chamber so often now, feel the warmth of my mother's body next to mine, when a thirst rages in my throat or a pain flares up, for no reason, somewhere in this half-wasted body.

From the window of Bibiji's chamber the tall minarets of the Badshahi Mosque were clearly visible. When they fought each other for the throne after my father's death, guns were mounted on those minarets and cannonballs flew over Hazuribagh and crashed into the Akbari gate. There was so much killing, Bibiji said, that rivers of blood flowed from the fort to the bazaar below and the people of

Lahore covered their ears with their hands and shut their eyes and lowered their heads and waited, on their knees, for the nightmare to pass.

I have read all there is to read about those days and years after my father's death; I know of the hundred and more treaties, letters, memoranda. And my mother told me of everything that I lost before I could understand what was mine by right. Some people who saw it all happen are still alive. Like Mangla Mai. I haven't seen her for so many years, but Arur tells me she is alive, in an ashram on the banks of the Ganges near Hardwar. She will remember everything—her memory was astonishing. She will understand my wish to die a different death. And also my other wish: to sleep, to forget, to be done with it.

Or perhaps even she won't. Nobody will understand why I am dying like this, alone, in this small hotel room, in a beautiful but strange city, from where I can see only the edge of a narrow cobbled street below and a thin strip of sky. The buildings across the street seem close enough to touch. Why am I here, denied all the wide open spaces of my life . . . the wheat fields that stretched away into the distance below the Lahore fort, the rolling countryside of Elveden?

Nobody will know how I fought—for I did, however imperfectly—and how I was defeated.

Arur Singh, winter 1905, Lahore fort

Once again, I have come to wander through my Maharaja's fort. Whenever the memories of the years that I served him faithfully, the memories of his struggle and his pain, assail me, I seek solace in these empty courtyards and gardens and havelis. He was a child here. He was also a king here, though only for a few years. Perhaps it is here that he still lives.

Two sons he had, and a third, poor child, who died. And I am not counting the boy he buried a day after he was born. But it was only this Arur Singh—call him what you will—valet, ADC, servant—who saw his last days. The Maharaja wanted to adopt me as his son. He said so many times, but he never actually did it.

What would it have mattered if he had? My love for him, his for me, would have remained unchanged. These bonds are not of the blood; they are stronger, forged in the kiln of trust. I have lived through him, and he has allowed me the ultimate intimacy of seeing him in his weakest moments; I have seen him rage in his helplessness, and I have seen him weep like a child.

He has gone. And many years have passed since he left us for the home of our great Father in the sky. And perhaps it is good that he went early. I have seen his suffering, I have witnessed his humiliation and loneliness. So much more painful for me, since I have seen too his days of glory. I am the first to admit that the Maharaja made mistakes, that there were times he let himself down, but then show me a man who has not. Especially if he is misled and misinformed as a child the way he was, by those who had undertaken—and signed treaties!—to protect him. He was an innocent led blindfolded through the by-lanes of deceit. Just a youth flattered, fattened and duped.

But for all the mistakes and compromises that he made, for all the temptations that he gave in to, his end should not have been as it was—locked up in a cheap hotel room, watching the sun rise beyond the window and slowly reach its height and then descend until the window darkened. That is all he did, often unable to move from his bed, barely able to eat or drink water without assistance. Unable to speak properly, or to write his letters. After his death, I came and poured my heart out to Mangla Mai in her ashram at Hardwar and we shared our grief—she, who had seen him when he was born, and I, who had seen him die.

Together we wondered what was truly his own in the life he had been given. Who were his people? And where were all the companions of his heyday when he was sinking? All the men who had come to Elveden for his magnificent shooting parties, or eaten and drunk with him at the Carlton Club or travelled with him to Italy and Paris and made much of him in Moscow—where were they? Or even those who had written to him from India, from Calcutta and Pondicherry, with promises and dreams. Not one of his sons or daughters came to be with him. Not even Ada, whom he had made his second Maharani and showered with love and gifts.

My Maharaja was alone, very alone, when he died. And today, as I watch British soldiers saunter along the ramparts of his fort, I wonder if his troubled soul, the soul that was never allowed to belong, has found peace anywhere.

Lady Lena Login, winter 1893, Felixstowe

It was Freddie's letter that told me of Duleep's sudden death in Paris. And then the telegram arrived telling me that the funeral would be held at Elveden on the 28th of October. I could not go for the funeral. I was shrouded in a deep and quiet grief. Duleep had been like a son to my husband, the late John Login, and me.

There are aspects of Duleep's life that only my husband, and therefore I, were privy to. After all, with God's grace, it had fallen to our lot to take care of him when he was just a tender child. After the annexation of Punjab, it was left to my husband to wind up Duleep's reign in Lahore, including the famed toshakhana. All the riches of the Lahore durbar—the jewels, the gold and silver, the precious relics, the armour and saddles, the illuminated manuscripts—passed through John's hands. He was Killah-ka-Malik, Lord of the Citadel. And through His mercy, the Lord gave him the strength to resist all temptation. The Lord then blessed us, at Fattehgarh, to become his instruments and to witness the miracle of the prince finding our true faith.

We stood at his elbow during his early years in England, when he was still finding his feet in our society. In many ways, and for many years, we were the only parents he knew. I consoled him like one consoles a child when his mother, that clever and once beautiful Maharani Jindan, died. I shared his joy when he married Bamba. Today I grieve for Duleep. His was a loving soul, unjustly treated. And the injustices that he suffered filled him with bitterness, even towards me in the end. I pray that there be peace upon him.

General Charles Carrol-Tevis, autumn 1893, Paris

I've seen many things in my time—wars, battles, conspiracies. I fought for the Sultan of Turkey, for the Khedive in Egypt, for the Prussians. The dozen and more medals on my tunic have all been earned in action and each tells its own story. But there never was anything like the Maharaja's case. I had never thought that my adventures would extend from the barracks of Pennsylvania to dreams of the Shish Mahal of Lahore ... It satisfied even *my* yearning for the exotic, my thirst for intrigue. I became the old fool's trusted Chief of Staff, or as he himself said, 'my only true private friend in Paris'. And I think I can say with complete confidence that no one knew better than me how the last few years of the Maharaja's life unfolded, in Paris and in Russia. I saw him fulminating against the British Crown in Reynold's Bar in Paris and I saw him come back from Moscow, defeated and without a hope in the world. Those years I shared all his moments of madness. I even became the first witness to sign the marriage register when he wed that Englishwoman, Ada.

I've been told I'm a hard man, and I take pride in that. Tenderness and tears and wailing are for men like the Maharaja of nowhere who was so full of complaints and confusion, so without iron in his soul, that he wouldn't see deceit and disaster till he'd been gutted and the assassin was breathing into his face. I pitied him sometimes, but more often I was fascinated by his talent for misfortune.

Book Two

THE SHISH MAHAL

Mangla, winter 1893, Hardwar

But you tell me now, Arur, that Duleep has gone to his God and you have buried him in Vilayat. Buried him! In the land of the firanghi! May you all perish in hell! We needed to bathe him and dress him like a king and cremate him, burn him on a pyre of sandalwood, then pray for mercy on his soul. He suffered all his life. Even in death he will not find peace. He will wait forever to be one with the dust of his Punjab.

Forever, Arur, do you know how long that is?

I am old now but I still have the power of the inner eye. I know it will be forever. I know that grass will grow long over his grave in the rain and the cold. The firanghis will forget who he was, forget his lost kingdom. They will forget his story, his pain, his mother's broken heart. It will be only a rare son of Punjab who will go all the way to bow before him, to put a flower on his grave, fold his hands and say the Waheguru's prayer for the soul of the Maharaja of Punjab. That Vilayat, I hear, is only a small country with nullahs and not even one proper river. How will one who should have ruled over the mighty five rivers of Punjab find peace there?

Who would have guessed when he was born that this would be his end. Where was it you said that he died, Arur, which strange city? Not even in Vilayat where at least he had his sons and daughters. But in some hell where there was no one to pray for him during his last moments, no one to hold his hand and shut his eyes!

How different from that Bhadon evening of long ago when the news of his birth was brought to the lion, Maharaja Ranjit Singh. Our Sarkar's joy knew no bounds and Lahore dissolved in music and celebrations. We got together in the pavilion where he was born, just across the terrace from the Sheran-wala hammam. Kashmiri dancing girls with their large noserings, and gold coins at the ends of their plaits, performed all evening for Rani Jindan, and the other queens

13

came with their own slave girls to see the young prince, to give Jindan pearls and jewels and warm hugs. I felt no less than a queen myself that day.

The Sarkar sat in the beautiful Hazuribagh baradari, surrounded by his durbar, and listened to the shabads being sung by the raagis.

'We will call him Duleep, after the great saint of Thanesar. May Waheguru give him the same wisdom,' he said.

Then sweets, fruits, milk with almonds and sherbet were brought out for the nobles from the gulabkhana and all over the city, from the Taxali darwaza at one end to the Kashmiri darwaza at the other, the poor sat in long lines and were fed. Horsemen tossed coins from their bulging saddlebags in the crowded bazaars and a thousand and one cows were gifted to Brahmins. Guns roared in salute from the walls of the city. At night the lamps that lit up the Roshni darwaza were so bright that anybody looking towards Lahore from miles away in every direction would have known that something special was being celebrated in Ranjit Singh's court. That is how the Sarkar celebrated the birth of his favourite son. He must have felt a knife slice his heart in heaven, watching how his Duleep ended his days, alone and broken.

Kismet is the wretched mistress of us all. No, Arur, I did not want to hear the end of this story. Not I, I who saw the beginning.

It was a long time ago that I came to Lahore, a long time ago. I was very young but I still remember the night that I reached the city of my dreams, a city whose glory was to become my glory, at least for a while. They used to say in my village that he who has not seen Lahore has not been born. And it was true. The city had been the seat of so many emperors; I don't even know all their names. But my Lahore was the Lahore of Ranjit Singh. The city that had opened its doors like the welcoming arms of a courtesan to the young Sukerchekia. And he made it the queen of all the cities of the world, with the zamzamah gun guarding the Delhi darwaza and two caged lions outside the Sheran-wala darwaza. Pirs and bandits, beggars and merchants, women of high virtue and low—the lionheart's city was home to them all, they could make their fortune here or lose it. The splendour of Lahore, Arur, it is like a drug, and my Duleep ruled it once. How could little, frozen Vilayat ever be enough after that . . .

That early winter night, when I first arrived in Lahore with Jassa Munshi, I could not stop looking around me. My eyes moved in wonder from the walls of the fort to the minarets of the masjid, then to the towers of the palace. The streets and lanes buzzed with so much life; anything was possible here. It was like being in the spell of afeem! I was so happy that my feet hardly touched the ground as I followed Jassa Munshi to his house in Chowk Dara, near Delhi darwaza.

I could feel Heero Dei's beady eyes searching my face in the yellow lamplight as we ate. Jassa Munshi had told her that I was from Kangra as soon as we entered the house and he had said nothing more. Then he had washed his hands and told her to set his meal. After eating his fill, he had belched loudly, showing his satisfaction on getting a home-cooked meal after four days on the road and turned to Heero Dei again.

'Let her eat with you and show her where to sleep.'

She turned to me as soon as he left.

'Kangra girls are supposed to be very beautiful. Fair, rosy cheeks, sharp features, long black hair. You don't look like you are from Kangra.'

I did not say anything to the wretch. Clearly, she was not really important, just an old woman, perhaps an old relative, who kept house for the Munshi. I was hungry and I was eating, and that much was enough then. But I did stop to look at her full in the face. I knew that in my eyes she would see what weapon had helped me survive hunger, and the brutality of men. It was a good substitute for beauty.

She looked at me, saw the flame of the lamp flicker in my brown eyes and looked away. I knew she would keep her old mouth shut after that. My eyes would make her think before she said anything more. Today, these eyes are old and tired and lifeless. But those days, they were something.

The old witch tried another trick.

'You know who your father is?'

'Yes, Piru Mal.'

'What is he?'

'He is a Banda Farash.'

I enjoyed saying that. Heero Dei moved back as if I had struck her across the face.

'Hai, hai, the daughter of a slave dealer in our house! What is the Munshi doing? He has gone senile!'

'What do you expect him to do with me? He paid forty rupees, you know.'

Heero Dei clapped her palms over her ears.

'Bought you? From your own father!'

'No.'

I did not tell her that my father had actually sold me to a travelling mirasi for twenty-five rupees. The mirasi took me along from village to village, singing at weddings, making me twirl in front of strange drunken men. Always they would want me but the mirasi thought I was too young for them. Fool. He wanted to keep me for himself.

And in the nights he was tender and gentle with me. But in the end, he was greedy. When Jassa Munshi offered him forty rupees after my dance, he could not refuse and he left me there, standing in the middle of a wedding, not knowing to whom I belonged.

No, I did not tell her all that. I just continued to eat.

'Clean up after you,' she said. 'Don't behave like some newly-wed wife. You are just a new toy. He will tire of you soon.'

Then she told me where to sleep and shuffled away, the lamp held low over her head casting flickering shadows on the walls of the long corridor. I was to sleep on the floor near the chullah, not far from the Munshi's bed. But I was too excited to sleep. I opened the window that Heero Dei had shut and looked out.

All around me were double-storeyed houses, each with its own balcony, extending over the narrow street. Above the houses, the moon hung from the sky as if by a string, between the two minarets of the big masjid. Rani or concubine, beautiful or not, it no longer mattered. What mattered was that I had left Kangra forever and reached Lahore.

Of course, Jassa Munshi could not handle me. I was meant for bigger things. If I had come so far from my father's hut on the banks of the Beas where we had never seen the face of a silver coin, if I had escaped the old mirasi, it was not just to live as the mistress of Jassa Munshi in his hovel in Chowk Dara. He had paid forty rupees for me and that much I would serve him, but not a moment more.

Every time I looked at the narrow street, its smells and sounds called me. The lamps of the palace wove so many dreams in my head. And when the important Sardars passed through the lanes, on their camels and horses, dressed in their jewels and silks, their weapons glinting in the sun, I could not take my eyes off them. I wanted to be part of their world, the world of the katcherry and the harem, the world of kings and queens ...

But I must not forget that this is not my story. I have to tell my Duleep's story, and for me that began when I reached the fort, and my fate was tied to that of my clever beautiful Maharani Jindan.

In the afternoons, Heero Dei would sleep, senseless, in her darkened cool room at the end of the corridor, next to the angled window that caught every gasp of air that drifted across the plain from the Ravi. While she snored, I would step out. My face fully covered, I would step from shop to shop, duck under balconies, dodge into the narrow lanes. I had a sharp nose even then; I had found a place where the rich and powerful men gathered in the afternoons. It was the haveli of a rich munshi in Hira Mandi, kept only for pleasure. Big cool rooms with punkah-wallahs, silk curtains, soft shawls on the floor, musicians. I would dance for the munshi and his friends—the subedar, the tahsildar, the thanedar. They would laugh and drink and swoon, and they liked me. It doesn't take much to please rich old men and I knew all the tricks. Of course I got silver coins but I also got what I yearned for even more—gossip. News from the fort, even whispers about the palace. Whose star was rising in the Sarkar's court and who was on his way out.

And then, before the sun sank below the ramparts of the fort and the evening star rose above the minaret of the Badshahi Masjid, before that old crone woke from her siesta, wracked by her black cough, I would return to the house.

Of course they found out soon enough. Too many tongues wagged in those bazaars. Jassa Munshi thundered into the house, frothing at the mouth. Without warning he caught me by my hair and dragged me into the deodhi.

'You whore!' he shouted. 'Where have you been going to in the afternoons? I know everything. The entire bazaar is laughing at me.

Jassa brought a girl and everybody is enjoying her, they say. This is how you thank me for bringing you to Lahore? I will teach you.'

My cheek stung under his slap and I had to bite my lip to stop my tears.

'What else did you expect from the daughter of a slave trader?' Heero Dei spat out the words from where she stood in the doorway. I could see victory in her eyes. 'Kanjari! Throw her out, before it is too late even for that.'

Jassa Munshi was staring at me. I could see that he did not know what to do.

'Throw her out!' Heero Dei screamed again.

Then he caught me by my hair once more and pushed me out of the door. It shut with a bang behind me and suddenly, once again, I belonged to nobody.

I went straight to Shabbo Bai's terrace after that, deep in Moti Bazaar, just short of the Masti darwaza. It was a very crowded area, small houses and lanes so narrow that the balconies of the houses almost touched each other. Travellers came in from the Masti darwaza and rested their horses and camels near the hammam. There they would bathe and sleep on large wooden beds and smoke hookahs. Many of them would come to Shabbo Bai's terrace to drink and dally with the girls.

Shabbo Bai looked on intently, her small black eyes glistening with greed, as I unknotted the corner of my shawl and took out two gold bangles. She weighed them in her hand, fingered the two elephants that formed the ends of the bangles and slipped them onto her arm.

'Turn around,' she said. 'Show me what you can do.'

I sang for her, I danced a bit, I used all the little tricks I knew.

She again weighed the gold bangles in her hand. They were heavy. I had invested most of the money that I had earned during my afternoon dances, in them. With the remaining I had got myself a necklace with a large panna and hanging earrings. But I wasn't going to give the old churail everything.

'All right,' she said. 'You can stay for a while. But don't get too ambitious. You don't have the beauty to compete with the others in these lanes.'

They used to call that lane the kanjarkhana; it was the place of the prostitutes. I never felt any shame living there; everybody who was anybody came there sometime or the other. Many years earlier, before I was even born, the Sarkar used to come there too. Those were the days when that beautiful kanjari Mauran had, with her curly black hair and her flashing eyes, danced her way into the young Maharaja's heart. He would come and not go; he would spend night after night in her rooms. Food and drink and royal clothes would be brought to him from the fort at night. And in the mornings he would ride out on his horse with her sitting in front, through the lanes at a gallop and out into the plain that led to the river. Nobody was allowed to accompany them. And the city, you well know, still talks of the way they used to play Holi, from the back of an elephant, coloured from head to foot themselves and throwing colour wildly on everyone they met in the bazaar. It was ishq the way only royalty enjoys it.

The people did not like it, but who would have risked the great Ranjit Singh's wrath? Only an old noble took it upon himself to advise the Maharaja.

But there was hot blood in the Sarkar's veins then and he was drunk on Mauran's songs and dances. He took away the old man's title, confiscated his lands and fined him ten thousand rupees. Ten thousand rupees! It was a fortune. Somehow the old man borrowed the money and freed his lands but he did not live long after that; he died of a broken heart.

Finally, the Sarkar married Mauran and took her away into the fort and stopped coming to the kanjarkhana. The senior ranis protested but did he care! Mauran began to light up the fort every night with her songs and dances. But there was one power to whom even Ranjit Singh would bow—the power of the Khalsa Panth. The Sikh King of Punjab with a Musalman prostitute! The keepers of the faith were furious. The command came from the Akal Takht at the Harmandir Sahib in Amritsar. But look at the greatness of Ranjit Singh. He went, not like a king, but as an ordinary humble Sikh and folded his hands and apologized. When the Gurumata was issued that he should be given a hundred lashes, he took off his shirt and they tied him to a tree. But who was going to lash a lion? The people loved him; the Sikh warrior holding the lash touched him lightly on the back and untied him. But Ranjit had kept the honour of the Khalsa. He knew that his Guru's power lay with the people. All his life he never acted like a despot, though he was all-powerful ...

But I digress—I am an old woman now, distracted by tragedy ... Anyway, I didn't have to stay too long at Shabbo Bai's. One day, the water carrier at the palace, Topi Mushki, came for me. When Shabbo Bai called me, I could see that she wasn't too happy.

'What's happening? People from the palace are coming to ask for you. Looking at you, I wouldn't have thought so.'

I had entertained one of Topi Mushki's friends a few days earlier, a traveller who had come in through the Masti darwaza. He had spent a happy evening with me and left me a fistful of precious Afghani stones. He sang my praises to Mushki who decided to come and see for himself. Soon he became so fond of me that he took me away to live with him in the fort. I had finally risen above the lanes and the bazaars.

Topi Mushki had a handsome young nephew, Gulloo. With his sharp features, glowing complexion, jet-black hair, he was heartbreakingly handsome. When he walked through the gardens and quadrangles of the fort, his red silk scarf tied around his neck, his leather mushk of water resting easily on his powerful shoulders, there were many young girls, and who knows, even some of the ranis, who eyed him with desire.

He moved in and out of the zenana and could be seen swaggering in the courtyards, grinning at the girls. The rogue had even charmed the Sarkar, who was kind to him. He even let the rascal ride some of his horses. I knew Gulloo's secret though; he would tell me when he came back to the house at night and ate the food that I would lay out for him. He had eyes only for the young Rani Jindan.

'I have seen her once without her veil, Mangla,' he said, 'and I understood why the Sarkar has married her even when he is no longer young. She is a beauty amongst the most beautiful.'

That I had heard too. The whole fort, the city beyond had heard it. The Sarkar had crossed fifty. He no longer had his old strength. The British had sent a doctor who was trying all sorts of new methods to revive his strength, even electric current. What was he

going to do with a young fireball like Jindan? Even then, he had
married her. Not in the way that he had married Gul Bahar Begum
just three years earlier, of course. Then there had been singing and
ceremonies and flowers everywhere. Jindan had come in quietly to
Lahore, married to an arrow and a sword sent to her village in
Gujranwala.

'I want to see her, Gulloo,' I told him.

He looked at me quietly.

'Why not? Maybe you will be more useful to me there than you
are at my uncle's house. You may be getting too much for him to
handle anyway.'

And so it was that one day, I presented myself to Rani Jindan.
She was only a junior rani and lived modestly in one room, while the
senior ranis had sets of rooms, corridors, balconies, gardens to
themselves. Of course they were not there all the time. They would
live on their jagirs or with their parents and come back to Lahore
when the Sarkar ordered. He didn't have too much time for them in
any case. All day he would be busy with the katcherry, foreign
visitors, his ghorcharhas, watching his infantry at parade, or with his
hunting and riding. And of course, there was no dearth of dancing
girls. He was very fond of his Kashmiri girls whom he would dress
up as warriors, with shields and swords and bows and arrows, and
when they rode into camp and the Sarkar made them fight with each
other, the Angrez visitors watched with their mouths hanging wide
open. Even in Vilayat they had never seen anything like that.

Gulloo had given me a bunch of large, freshly cut red roses from
the garden near the Barhi Khwabgah. I bent low before Rani Jindan
with folded hands.

'Who are you?' she asked, her voice young but confident. She
was new there, as new to being in a palace as I was. But she was even
then a queen.

'Mangla, Rani ji. Your slave, if you wish.'

'What lovely roses. Where did you get them?'

'An admirer of yours has sent them, Rani ji. Gulloo Mushki has
chosen them from the big gardens.'

I saw a tiny smile light up her large eyes. Perhaps it was not the
first time that she had got those roses. There are stories, and I know

you've had to hear more than me, Arur ... They were beautiful, those two, and young; to see them was to know the magic of that jaadugar in the heavens. So there were stories ... But no one ever dared say things to my face ...

The Rani liked me instantly. Otherwise she would not have told me to come and go when I wished. Soon, as was only to be expected, old Jassa Munshi came to know that I had reached the fort. He must have thought that maybe he could make some money out of me, get some jewels in exchange. He landed up at the fort one day, puffing, his face red from the steep climb. There was a big scuffle with Gulloo.

'She is mine. All the way from Kangra I have brought her, paid for her, fed her and clothed her. And now you have become the owner?'

'Get away, Munshi, before I have you speared and hung.'

'Speared and hung! Who do you think you are? A prince, just because you carry water to these royal rooms?'

They were at each other's throats then. I had to step in and stop them otherwise Gulloo would have slaughtered the older man there and then.

'I will go to the Sarkar, if necessary,' screamed the Munshi as he fell on his back over the two steps that led from the house into the courtyard.

And so the Munshi did me another favour! I reached Summan Burj in Lahore fort. It was summer and though it was not yet noon, the marble floor with its yellow and blue squares burnt my feet. One could get blisters from that marble when the sun was at its height. I had never been in that courtyard before, never even dreamt of it. This was the centre of the kingdom of the Sarkar. With the Naulakha pavilion on one side, the fountains in the centre and the beautifully decorated Shish Mahal, with its double pillars and arches. From here, everything was made to happen. Here they took decisions to go to war or to sign agreements. Here they punished or forgave offenders, here the Sarkar was presented nazranas from far and wide and here he gave away fabulous gifts—land and horses, pearls, emeralds, rubies, Kashmiri shawls. From here he looked down across the plain towards the Ravi and he knew that as far as he could see, the kingdom was his. There was something magical about that place; a different breeze blew through that court.

The Sarkar himself was in a pure white robe and a white turban, sitting cross-legged on his throne. He always dressed simply and hardly ever wore any jewels except for a string of magnificent pearls, each as big as a marble, around his waist and the Koh-i-noor on his arm. Around him were his courtiers, his Wazir and his heir, all splendidly dressed, with their elaborate turbans and glistening beards. The sun bounced off their clothes of crimson and yellow, their jewels and their weapons. I could see through my veil that they were all busy admiring a horse that stood in the courtyard, saddled and bridled, ready to go, scraping the marble eagerly with its foot. I did not dare raise my face. I pulled my veil down and stared at my feet.

When the horse was taken away, the Sarkar turned to us.

'What is this, what's the matter?'

Gulloo stepped forward.

'Sarkar, it is a small matter.'

'Gulloo, you stole someone's girl? And you call it a small matter? You will never mend your ways, badmash.'

'Sarkar, I did not steal her. She came to me. She keeps my house.'

'What do you have to say?' the Maharaja turned to Jassa Munshi.

'If justice be done, huzoor, she is mine. I have paid forty full rupees for her in Kangra.'

There was a moment of silence and then, the Sarkar spoke again.

'Look up, girl, let us see why these two fools are fighting over you.'

Slowly I raised my veil and looked up, wishing that the marble floor would swallow me and at the same time wanting to look the Sarkar straight in the face. His one good eye rested on me for a moment and I think in that moment he measured me fully, my birth, my bearing, my capabilities.

'This girl has spirit; neither of you can handle her for long. Like a wild mare, she will toss you aside. She should stay with a rani.'

'She has already presented herself to Rani Jind Kaur, Maharaj,' said Gulloo.

'Good, let her stay with our Jindan. She is new here, she needs good help.'

He signalled to one of the men, who came and gave some gold coins to the Munshi.

It must have been a good amount, for the Munshi instantly spoke up.

'Sarkar, I bought her only for your service, I knew she was meant for the palace.'

That was it. That was how I got away from Jassa Munshi and also left Gulloo and his fat uncle. God gave me the great chance of serving kings and queens. I swore that I would serve Jindan till my dying breath.

I did not know, when I made myself that promise, how soon I would have to become much more than a trusted maid to my Rani, and to her child. Now it has taken months for me to get news of Duleep's death. But when the Sarkar lay dying, the news came to us instantly, in fluttering fearful whispers, as if countless butterflies were carrying it in all directions across the silent courtyards and gardens of the fort. Every hour new word came about his condition from Summan Burj. He had opened his one good eye. He had asked for water. He was being given a new English medicine. The Brahmins had started another yagya. Diamonds, gold, elephants were being given away . . .

Jindan would not move from the window. I was worried for her. She had not eaten a proper meal in two days.

'If not about yourself, at least think of the child, Rani ji. If you don't eat, or fall sick, who will protect him?' I said.

She glanced at him. The baby, the little Duleep, our precious Dula ji, was sleeping peacefully. His round face was bathed in moonlight.

'What will happen, Mangla?'

I knew she was scared. She was young, barely twenty, and she hadn't seen death. She hadn't been in the palace very long, either, where she had gained entry because of her charming ways and her father's wiliness. That old Manna Singh Aulakh was a clever one. He could say anything to the Sarkar, tease him, joke with him, because he took such good care of the royal dogs. It was said that Manna Singh would run alongside Ranjit's horse, carrying Jindan on his shoulder and shouting: 'Sarkar, this girl is becoming burdensome.

Make her your queen. Your harem is full of old women. You are young, aren't you? Or have you also given up your strength? If you are young, you need a young girl.' So one day the Sarkar put his chadar around Jindan and made her his rani, one of his many ranis. In no time at all, she had captivated him with her smiles and her spirit. It was difficult to take one's eyes off her face, so magical was her beauty. And when she walked, it was with the grace of a young tigress. She knew how to please a man; oh yes, she had all the guiles.

'I don't know what will happen,' I replied to her, standing at the window with her when the Sarkar was on his deathbed. 'But whatever it is, we will see difficult days. We will have to take care of ourselves, Rani ji, and the young prince.'

'Kanwar Kharak Singh will be Maharaja, won't he?'

'That is already decided.'

This had been decided more than twenty years earlier. Kharak Singh was the Sarkar's eldest son, as you know, from Raj Kauran, daughter of the Nakkai clan. He was weak and given to opium and not a patch on his legendary father. Perhaps that is why the other pretenders to the throne did not give up. The eldest queen, Mehtab Kaur, egged on by her ambitious mother, put forward her twins, whom the Sarkar had acknowledged but probably never fathered. Of these, Sher Singh's claim was more serious, because the other brother, Tara Singh, was an imbecile. To quell all doubts, the Sarkar had proclaimed Kharak Singh to be the Kanwar. To his mind the line of succession must have been clear. Kharak Singh would be followed by his son, the brave and handsome Naunihal Singh. So once again, as he lay dying, the lionheart put the raj tilak on Kharak Singh's forehead while the important courtiers watched. The ghorcharhas, the Sarkar's brave and unruly irregulars, galloped out of the fort in four directions, reading out the announcement wherever people gathered to listen to them:

'The Maharaja has granted full power to Shahzada Kharak Singh over all the protected state under the Sarkar and over the troops of horsemen and footmen and the topkhana ... And the Kanwar has decided that Raja Dhian Singh will continue as Wazir.'

Wazir-e-Azam, Raja Kalan Bahadur, Raja-e-Rajgan, Ujjal Didar, Nirmal Budh, Muqqurrab-i-Bargah—Dhian Singh, our all-powerful Prime Minister had many titles. Do you know of him, Arur? You weren't born when he was at the height of his glory. Ranjit Singh did not take a step without seeking counsel from his handsome Wazir. He and his two brothers Gulab Singh and Suchet Singh, Dogras from Jammu, had joined the Sarkar as mere troopers. But such had been their ability and bravery that they had quickly earned his trust. The Sarkar trusted all manner of men. His courtiers included men like these Dogra brothers, Muslims like Fakir Azizuddin, Brahmins from lands to the east, and those firanghi jarnails, Ventura and Avitable. His fellow Sikh Jats, who had been his comrades in arms during his campaigns, were represented only by a few prominent families like the Sandhawalias, Attariwalas and the Majithias. Their blood boiled at the dominance of the outsiders; they believed they owned Punjab, that they alone had a claim on Ranjit Singh and all his kingdom. Of course such resentment could only end in bloodshed. And it did, after the Sarkar was gone . . .

That night—the night before the lion was taken away from us—we sat near that window, Jindan and I, queen and slave, with the child Duleep between us, and looked out into the hot still darkness, towards the light that flickered in the Sarkar's chambers. There was an uneasy silence that had spread over the fort and the city. I have noticed this many times: when death is at hand, silence takes over. The gates of the fort had been ordered shut by Wazir Dhian Singh and even the shops in the city had not opened all day. The lanes were deserted and people stayed away even from the balconies. The lamps at Roshni darwaza had not been lit for four evenings.

'Maybe the English medicines can do something,' the Rani murmured next to me. 'Yesterday things seemed better. But today I have little hope. What will happen to us? What will happen to my son?'

That night Jindan wouldn't let me go to my sleeping quarters across the courtyard.

'Stay here,' she commanded me, 'I am scared.'

When I woke up the next morning, I realized that for the first time I had slept in the same room as a rani! Jindan was still sleeping.

Tobah! What beauty! Even I, a woman, could not take my eyes off that face as she lay on the bed, one arm covering her son, her long black hair falling in thick waves from her pillow. Gently I drew a sheet over her fair feet with their heavy gold panjebs and left the chamber. I wanted her to rest; instinctively I knew that the day that was rising would be a very difficult one. Then tying up my own hair, I walked in the cool breeze of the dawn across the courtyard to my room. I needed to get the latest news from the Sarkar's bedchamber.

There was a whisper sizzling among the slave girls. The Sarkar had wanted to give away the Koh-i-noor diamond to the Jagannath ji temple. It was his dying wish. But it was not being carried out. The clever men around him were already showing their true colours, and this when there was still breath in the body of the old lion. When the Sarkar had been in good health, there was not a man in all Punjab who would have tarried to carry out his order. I had heard that once he had even fined the great warrior Sham Singh Attariwala fifty thousand rupees for not following a firman. And now when he had signalled that he wanted to give away the diamond that he used to wear on his right arm, not a man had moved. They had made excuse after excuse—the priest said that the command had been given to the Wazir; the Wazir said that it was for the Kanwar to decide; the Kanwar said that the diamond was in the possession of the guardian of the toshakhana who in turn said that it was in Amritsar.

A deep furrow, they said, had marked the dying Sarkar's forehead as he lay there while they argued. All his faithfuls were not willing to let him buy some more moments of life. The diamond was his; it had been used before to buy a life. He had taken it from the Afghan, Shah Shuja, after ensuring the Afghan's life. I tell you, they should have let the wretched thing go to Jagannath ji. It would have been better than letting the Angrez Malka take it. At least it would have remained in Hindustan. They gave away a lot of other things—lakhs of rupees, fully decorated horses, elephants with gold and silver howdahs, hundreds of cows with gilded horns, golden saddles, pearls, gold necklaces.

But by then it was too late for even the gods to intervene.

We live through many nights in our lives, all kinds of nights—black moonless nights, stormy nights, full moon nights brighter than

some days, nights of love, nights when the heart is about to burst
with the pain of separation . . . but we forget them all. What we do
not forget are the nights of death. When a life comes to an end, not
only that one body but everything around one goes dead—the air,
the animals and the birds, the trees. Such was the night when Ranjit
Singh died. I have not forgotten a moment of that long night.

Jagged lightning flashed across the sky over the Ravi, over the
thick jungles where the Sarkar used to hunt, over the banks where he
used to ride along the water, watching its spirited flow, testing the
paces of his favourite horses. It flashed over the groves of mango and
shisham where he used to rest and over the grounds where he used
to watch his troops at parade or entertain his Angrez visitors,
challenging them to feats of tent-pegging, riding and drinking. The
lightning did not reach the walls of the fort. It seemed a black shroud
had been flung over us.

The wailing of the ranis pierced the darkness. The spirit had
flown from the sick body. The lion lay on the ground, like any
ordinary man, his hair and body washed with Gangajal, dressed in
his new clothes for his journey into the next world. Around him, the
Kanwar, the Wazir and other courtiers were tearing their hair,
banging their foreheads against the stone walls, lamenting the end of
an age. How many of these men were pure of heart we will never
know, but at that moment their grief was true and terrible. That is
the kind of power that great men have, on friend and foe alike.

My heart pained for Jindan. I knew, instinctively, what was
going through her head. And I knew I had to stop her. Else, I too
would be finished.

'Sati is not your dharma,' I told her, standing beside her as she
prepared to join the other queens, all gathered in mourning. 'Sati is
for the Hindu queens if they wish. Let them burn if they want. You
are the daughter of Sikh Jats, this is not your tradition. And remember
your dharma now is towards your little child. You cannot leave him.'

I knew my Rani could be impetuous, and too proud to let
anyone show her to be a lesser person. In the great and public
tragedy of the Maharaja passing away, she wouldn't be the junior of
any of his ranis. I had to hold her back long enough to let her blood
and the fires of her grief and fear cool, long enough for her instinct
for life to regain control of her mind.

Jindan's beautiful large eyes were red with crying as she turned towards me.

'Mangla, we will be lost without the Sarkar's protection,' she said.

For the first time that night, I had the courage to firmly hold her by the elbow.

'Rani ji, you are a Sikh, a woman of courage and there is greater courage in living than in dying. We will only be as lost as the rest of Punjab. The Sarkar himself has put us under the care of Raja Suchet Singh. He owes all that he has to the Sarkar, he will protect us.'

I was not exaggerating. Dogra Suchet Singh, like his brothers, was not born a raja. He had been made a raja by Ranjit Singh. I picked up Duleep from his cradle. He was sleeping peacefully as if nothing had happened. Children are fortunate, they do not know what they have lost until they grow up. I handed him gently to his mother. She took one look at his face, took him in her arms and clutched him to her breast. In her eyes I saw a steely resolve, a look that I was to see many times in the years to come.

I knew then that we were safe.

In the bazaar, they were already preparing the sandalwood ship, decorated with gold and silver and fitted with sails of silk-embroidered shawls, that would carry the Sarkar into the next world. He would have been happy with that; he loved such things. When that Angrez Gardona sahib built him a boat, he had instantly filled it with jewelled dancing girls and floated down the Ravi, clapping his hands above his head in delight.

While the carpenters hammered away all night, the prayers continued. Sometimes the mantras of the Brahmins were louder than the chantings from the Granth, sometimes it was the other way round. And every once in a while, the wailing of the ranis rose above all else. Somehow that awful night passed and when dawn broke, the Sarkar was taken to the takhtgah, the hall with many pillars. That was where the people of the fort, all the courtiers and the jarnails, the ranis and the slaves would pay their last respects. It was only then that the news was allowed to spread beyond the gates of the fort: Maharaja Ranjit Singh had passed on. Like a poisonous snake, it slithered and raced through the sleeping bazaars and mohallas and then beyond the walls of the city. Travellers carried it from village to village, spies rode hard across the plain dotted with ruins of Mughal masjids and havelis. Soon everybody had heard it—the Sikh chieftains, the ordinary peasants, the English laats. The greatest son of the Sukerchekias was gone. Our world, it seemed, had come to an end.

Duleep Singh, autumn 1893, Paris

He was a wise one, my father, and a very brave man. All my life I could not muster up a trace of that wisdom or that courage in myself. Sometimes I feel like I am not his son at all and then I begin to think that perhaps Lord Dalhousie was not wrong when he said that I had been fathered by a bhisti. At other times I feel that no son of his could have matched him, for men like him are not born in every generation. It is too much for the best of men, too crushing an inheritance.

At an age when I was only hunting pheasants and partridge, Ranjit Singh had, through marriages or battles, made the Sukerchekia misl the strongest among the twelve feudal confederacies that the Sikh peasants had been divided into. Lahore became his prized possession when he rescued twelve guns from the Jhelum in flood for the departing Afghan Shah Zaman. The grateful Shah granted him the city and the district and the people of Lahore were only too glad to open their gates to my father. Then there was no stopping him. Kasur, Kangra, Multan, the hill kingdoms, the Baluch tribal tracts, Kashmir, Ladakh, the Pathan deras across the Indus, Peshawar—all became part of his empire. Commanding the Khyber Pass, he even controlled the destinies of the rulers of Kabul. But on the east he had the wisdom to recognize the power of the British. He accepted, in 1809, that the river Sutlej would be his boundary, with the exception of the strip of territory that he already owned on its eastern bank. To this alliance he remained truthful to the last, like I remained loyal to the British for decades. But they waited till they were strong enough and then they planned and plotted against him, like they did against me.

Perhaps I am his son after all.

Mangla, winter 1893, Hardwar

I held Duleep in my arms as the funeral procession started towards Roshni darwaza. How small, how innocent he was. Just nine months old. I used to hold him so close, like he was my own child. I haven't set my eyes on him now for nearly fifty years, ever since that day when I was turned out of Lahore. But I followed his every move. I knew when he was taken away to Shala Bagh from Lahore, his child's heart enticed by colourful toys while his mother was moved in the thick of the night to be imprisoned in the fort at Sheikhupura, never to return to her beloved Lahore. I also heard when that badmash Angrez, Login, took him Jumna paar, away to that godforsaken Fattehgarh and made him a Christian. I didn't touch food or water for many days when I heard that news; it curdled my heart.

Once when they were passing through Roorkee on their way from Fattehgarh to the hills, I even tried to meet him. But that haramzada Login did not permit it. They were afraid of me, afraid that somehow I would take him away, reunite him with Jindan, make him Maharaja again. How could I have? I only wanted to see him, and hold him close to me as on the day of the Sarkar's funeral.

He slept in my arms that day, peaceful and unaware, as I fanned his face. Jindan was in the zenana with the other ranis. I knew what would be happening there. The poor unfortunates who were going to commit sati would be getting ready, dressing up in jewels and silks. They would have convinced themselves that soon they would all become devis. But I had made Jindan swear by her son that she would live.

I covered my head as the funeral procession passed below the balcony. The raagis were singing shabads in front. Behind them was a group of Brahmins, their chests bare but for their holy threads, their heads shaved, tilaks on their foreheads, and alongside, the maulvis with their long hennaed beards. Then came the Sarkar himself in his golden sandalwood ship. It seemed to me that he was only sleeping and at any moment he would wake up, clap his hands, laugh out loud at the tamasha that was going on, call for Laili, climb into the saddle and ride off, leaving only the cloud of dust raised by the mare's hooves. He would become one with the mare and everybody would forget that he was a small-built man with only one good eye; he would become the wind itself.

But the ship passed through the lane and he slept on.

One after the other, the palanquins of the four ranis passed below me. The beautiful Guddan, she of my Kangra hills, my beautiful Katoch princess, daughter of Raja Sansar Chand. The Sarkar had married her and her sister Rani Raj Banso in Jwalamukhi temple, like a Hindu. Raj Banso did not live too long, poor thing, but Rani Guddan was happy. She had a large haveli in Nadaun, on the Beas. Once every few months she would come to Lahore. But now she would burn with him. And the others, Hardevi, Raj Kanwar, Banali, all beautiful, too young to die. But it was their wish, their tradition. I thanked God under my breath that my Jindan was not among them. One by one they were carried down the lane, distributing gold coins and jewels to the poor who lined the lanes.

I folded my hands and said my own last goodbye to the Sarkar. If he had set eyes on me that day, he would almost certainly not have known who I was. I would have been just a dancing girl for him, just a plain-looking kanjari. Dancing girls, slave girls, attendants came and went in the hundreds through that durbar. We were all sorts, the most beautiful, the not so beautiful and the ordinary, bought and traded by the kanjars. A girl could go for fifteen rupees or for two hundred and sometimes for almost nothing like when the famine struck Kashmir and hundreds of poor girls came down to the plains. Some were novices, some trained from infancy. The best ones, the ones with the softest, fairest skin, the sweetest voice, the best dancing ada, would be kept for the princes and the nobles. They would come into the Maharaja's zenana and the havelis of the Dogras and the Sardars. They would come as nazrana, they would come as prize of battle. And then, after a few years, when they were nineteen or twenty, they would be sent back to where they had come from, with some jewels and clothes and money. The prettiest and the clever ones would retire with a small jagir, a few hundred square yards of land, a small house, one or two faithful rich meherbaans. Some would refuse to go back; Lahore would have entered their blood by then. Even if they could no longer stay in the zenana of the Sarkar to entertain him or his sons or his firanghi jarnails or his

Angrez guests, they did not want to leave the city. So they would move out, buy a house in the lanes, hire their own musicians and set up their own kotha.

He would not have remembered me, our Sarkar, but I knew that I owed everything to him. What would the prayers of a kanjari matter to the greatest king of all Punjab? But I prayed for him, for his soul to find the True One.

From the terrace it seemed as if all of Lahore, rather all Punjab, had turned up to see the Sarkar's last journey on earth. Like the last sigh of a dying world, the smoke rose from the ship as the straw mats that covered not only his body but also the four ranis caught fire from the flame in Kanwar Kharak Singh's hand. There were slave girls too, seven of them. Nobody even remembers their names. Except that of Kaulan. This was their kismet. Poor, young girls, all younger than I was.

We could not see what exactly was happening beside the pyre. But soon word was flying back to us over the walls of the fort and through the gardens and even before the smoke had reached the heavens, the zenana knew what exactly had happened. The women sat in groups in the halls, sobbing, consoling each other.

And when the crowd dispersed, the stories began to flow through the bazaars. Each tongue added its own twist, as always happens. They say it is easier to stop a galloping mare than a wagging tongue.

'Even the birds and animals of Punjab are grieving. Did you see the two pigeons that flew into the pyre?'

'There was not a touch of fear on Rani Guddan's beautiful face. The last of her jewels she handed to the Brahmins as she climbed the pyre and put the Sarkar's head in her lap.'

'Dhian Singh, poor loyal Dhian Singh, he wanted to finish himself with the Maharaja. He threw himself on the pyre so many times, four times, five times.'

'Everybody stopped him. Kharak Singh, the Sardars, all threw their turbans at his feet.'

'Devi Guddan put Dhian Singh's hand in Kharak Singh's and made them both swear on the Sarkar's dead body that they will rule us together.'

'Don't be fooled! It is just the plain deceit of the Dogras. These brothers will finish us, divide Punjab between themselves. They hate the Sikhs. Men like Dhian Singh don't burn themselves; they let thousands go to their deaths before they go themselves.'

To cool the ashes of the Maharaja and his four wives, of those poor unnamed seven girls, and of the two pigeons, a huge cloud rose that afternoon from the Ravi and a light drizzle fell over the fort and the city. It was no ordinary drizzle. It was a last benediction, a farewell meherbaani of our Sarkar.

For thirteen days all Punjab mourned. Not a soul stirred in the lanes of Lahore, not a shop was open in its bazaars. Only the grain shops opened on the fourth day so that people could get their provisions. That day, Kanwar Kharak Singh and all the courtiers went back to the cremation grounds. The Kanwar sprinkled Gangajal to cool the smouldering pyres and with his own hands began to pick the ashes. They put the Sarkar's ashes in a bag sewn out of deerskin. Prayers were held before the Guru Granth and for two days the chiefs and the ranis made their last prostrations. Then they took the ashes away in his favourite palki to Hardwar. Kharak Singh rode alongside the palki. The crowds showered flower petals on the procession. The topkhana discharged its cannonballs and the blue smoke could be seen from far away.

The soldiers lined up for miles, swords glinting in their hands. The Sarkar had turned them from wild horsemen into the disciplined Khalsa army, had them trained by firanghi jarnails and taught them all there was to know of the business of war. My heart used to tremble just to look at that army. Among them were also the fierce Nihangs, whose fathers had put Ahmed Shah Abdali to shame and had helped Ranjit Singh conquer every fort they set their eyes on. Their valour was known even in Vilayat. They lined the big road in grief that day, some of them weeping like little orphans.

I tried to tell Rani Jindan that we should not leave Lahore. It was best to stay near the throne and wait to see what happened. Who knows what turn events would have taken if we had stayed there. Who knows what Duleep's destiny would have been then. But I was only, you must remember, a slave girl. I was not meant to decide these things. Raja Suchet Singh was our karta dharta. Our Sarkar had assigned us to his care. He would decide.

'I would strongly advise you to go away to Jammu for a while. It will be safer for you and the child,' I heard him telling Jindan in the zenana, a few days after the Sarkar's ashes had been immersed at Hardwar.

Suchet Singh was a picture. Tall, well built and fair, he had not yet seen thirty years. Younger and better looking than his two brothers, though not half as clever, his pleasing manners had brought him close to the Sarkar. He had three dashing friends—all ghorcharhas—four young happy-go-lucky riders. The Sarkar called them char yaar and gave them fine horses. A dera soon grew around them, headed by Suchet Singh—the charyaari dera, full of handsome, gallant men, who twisted their moustaches in tight curls, combed their beards up towards their ears and flaunted expensive daggers and pistols.

When Suchet Singh rode out to the Sarkar's durbar in full dress, the eye couldn't bear to rest upon him. Bright yellow silk shirt and three shawls—blue, white and red—twisted tightly below his helmet and across his back. A steel armour inlaid with rubies and diamonds. Jewelled sword and gun glinting with gold. And on his back a shield of rhinoceros skin and gold. I don't know where he'd got it from. But when his end came even that didn't save him . . .

Oh, Arur Singh! What have you started me on? What forgotten stories and conversations come back to me to trouble me in my old age! I thought that was all behind me, those golden years of Lahore, that dream-life when I was so close to great power and so much beauty. To so much that was a prelude to tragedy. Our Duleep's misfortunes began in all that glory. That is how kismet plays games with us. Look at me now—drawn back to the world and its maya as if I never renounced it. But the gods will forgive this old jogan . . . it is the love of a mother, for I was his mother, too, Arur. And I must relive those days, days of intrigue, violence, bloodshed and pain, all in memory of my Dula ji.

'No, Mangla,' Jindan told me when I said that we must stay on in Lahore. 'Here it will be the time of the ranis and the zenana of Kharak Singh, and then of his son, Naunihal. Who knows—perhaps Sher Singh will stake a claim some day. The Sandhawalia Sardars may try to challenge the influence of the Dogras. We will have no place here. I see only chaos, and we'll gain nothing from it. We may, in fact, be in danger. In the care of the Dogra Rajas, we should be safe, at least for the time being. Duleep will also get a childhood of peace.'

I had to agree. Jindan's mind had quickly perceived the truth; sometimes I thought she had a man's mind. Duleep was nowhere near the throne; he had no chance. But I was in love with the havelis and gardens of the fort, with the bazaars of Lahore. I had reached there with such difficulty. I did not want to leave it all and go away. And who knew how things would play out in Lahore? A lion had died, the jackals would now come out to prowl. Everybody knew Kharak Singh was a weak man. In any case it would be important to know everything that went on in the durbar. There was only one person who would always tell the truth: Shah Mohammed of Masti darwaza.

Shah Mohammed was a poet, a dervish, an admirer of the Sarkar. He walked the lanes, gathered all the news about the court and put it down on paper in such words that it seemed he was writing the stories of Lahore with his blood. Everybody in the bazaar knew him, with his henna-coloured beard and his high cap, his stooped low walk and, most of all, through his words. You could hear a line or a couplet and know in a moment that none but Shah Mohammed could have written that. He would always write, I knew that. He could not live if he did not.

But I had to convince him to write for us so that we knew all that happened at the durbar, all that could be of interest to Jindan, and to Duleep.

It was dark when I reached his alcove near Masti darwaza.

'Mian ji,' I told him, 'the Rani will pay. We need to get news of the durbar when we are in Jammu. There is no one else whose words paint scenes of such truth that one can see everything happening before one's eyes. Shah Mohammed's words need to reach us.'

Shah Mohammed put down his quill and turned to his hookah as if he had not heard me. I could hear his breath pulling the tobacco through the water. Then he ran a hand thoughtfully over his long beard and looked at me for a long moment. 'Is this Rani Jindan's firman or your idea?'

'I have no ideas of my own,' I lied. 'I am just a slave of the Rani.'

Those early days in Jammu were perhaps the best, the most innocent that Duleep Singh ever knew, although I am sure he must have forgotten them by the time you met him in Vilayat. So much happened to him, poor child, in the years that followed. Or perhaps he did not forget it all. One never knows what remains hidden somewhere in a child's mind, which long-lost sunlight gives him warmth on troubled nights . . .

In the haveli that we lived in there was a wide open courtyard with apple trees where the little prince learnt to walk. When he took those first three halting steps and fell forward, my heart leapt with joy.

'Rani ji, today is a very auspicious day for all of us. The prince has taken his first steps. May the Waheguru give him a long life.'

She slipped off a gold bangle and pressed it into my hand.

'God bless you, Mangla. Keep the evil eye off him.'

The haveli was on a gentle hill above the Tawi river. Across the clear water was the mud fort with its towers and four guns. Sometimes, we saw riders fording the river and going up the slope to the fort's gate. But nothing much seemed to happen there. The yellow flag of the Sikhs had flown over that fort for many years—our Sarkar had put it under the charge of Dogra Gulab Singh and his brothers.

We would sit in the sun, I combing the Rani's long black tresses for hours, others pressing her feet, while she lay with her eyes half closed watching the young girls vying with each other to carry Duleep, teach him to walk. The young prince was her joy and her consolation. His antics kept her from thinking of the days in Lahore when death had stilled the air, and robbed her of the lionheart's protection and of her good fortune.

Once every afternoon, the beautiful carriage with the four horses would be brought out and we would go out for a ride. Rani Jindan would sit in the front seat, holding Dula ji, in his golden turban, little pearl earrings and a quilted scarlet coat studded with

gems. We would ride along the river, watching the sun swirling in its
waters, the birds skimming its surface. Often we would ride the
other way, towards the forest grove. There, on the branches of the
bor tree we had strung out our swings. The girls would push each
other higher and higher, their long plaits swinging behind them, and
the Rani and I looked on, as the little prince watched them, his eyes
rolling as he followed the swings high into the sky.

And in the evening, if Jindan agreed, we would gather in a circle
around her in the courtyard and sing. We were still in mourning so
we sang sad songs. On most nights we sang the Heer. She loved that;
she said it made her cry.

> Look, the four corners of my scarf are empty; look, there is no
>   gold,
> No jewels, not half a coin, tucked in between its folds.
> I find no pleasure and no pride, in the pretensions of a bride.

But every few weeks, Jindan would become preoccupied with
thoughts of Lahore. 'I wonder how things are, Mangla,' she would
say.

I shared her yearning to know what was happening in Kharak
Singh's court. At such times our heart would no longer be in the
afternoon ride or the songs.

From the haveli's balcony, I would keep a lookout for the
runner from Lahore. And when finally he appeared in the distance,
taking long steps down the path that emerged from the trees on the
lower slopes of the hills, bare bodied except for his loincloth, a
leather bag slung across his bursting chest, I would rush down the
wooden steps to tell Jindan.

Quickly a ghara of water, a large gadwi of lassi, a pile of freshly
made rotis, daal and dahi would be put out for him in the courtyard.
No matter how impatient we were for the news, we would wait until
he had drunk and eaten and wiped the sweat from his body. Then
he would unsling his leather bag and pull out the folded sheets of
paper that had come all the way from Lahore, passed on hand to
hand by five others like him. He would bow low before the Rani
where she sat in the shade of the veranda and hand the papers over
to me. I would give him a silver coin and he would withdraw, to go

and sleep in the quarters of the guards. I loved holding those sheets of paper; it was like holding Lahore in my fingers with all its gossip, its excitement, its grandeur.

All the news of those days after the Sarkar's passing, we got this way.

Wrote Shah Mohammed:

Bhadon, the eighteenth day.

The Maharaja's ashes have not yet cooled in the Ganga and what we feared has already begun. The enemies of Maharaja Ranjit Singh must be rejoicing. Prince Sher Singh should have come to Lahore before the Lion died but he tarried in Batala, not wanting to endanger his life lest Raja Dhian Singh had hatched some scheme against him. But now he is possessed with new courage. He rides across Punjab seeking support where he can. He tried to take the fort of Kangra. Then he tried to get the support of the British; he even promised them a part of the territory beyond the Sutlej if they helped him . . . Oh, the fate of our Punjab! Its own sons speak the unthinkable, ready to sell it.

Today, the eighteenth day of Bhadon, Kharak Singh was adorned with the tilak of the Badshahi in the Chahil Sutoon, the hall with the forty pillars. Mughal emperors—Akbar and Jahangir—used to give audience in that hall, dispense justice . . . But their time has gone.

All time passes, only fools forget that.

Kharak Singh was bathed in the waters of the Ganga and of the seven other sacred rivers. The purohit led the puja. Then the Sikh granthis applied the kesar tilak to the Maharaja as he sat in white clothes, wearing the Koh-i-noor on his arm like the late Sarkar. And this time Sher Singh came. He was received most cordially and given all honours, more than anybody else in the takhtgah. But Kanwar Naunihal Singh was absent. A few days ago his parwana from Peshawar had reached all the Sardars at the court: Hold on, it had said. Do not conduct the tilak ceremony of my father till I return. I am on my way.

But they say that Dhian Singh did not want to wait. He wanted Kharak Singh to be safely on the throne before his hot-blooded young son entered Lahore.

Strange are the days in which we live, a father fears his son, a son will not trust his father.

Asu, the sixth day.

The pledges taken over the pyre of the Sarkar have been forgotten; a divide has come about between Kharak Singh and Dhian Singh and it widens like the Ravi in the rains. Kharak Singh's old fears about the Dogras surface now like poisonous snakes. The Maharaja has found new advisers; the chief among them is Chet Singh Bajwa. Young and blessed with good looks, alert as an eagle, he walks fearlessly in the durbar. He has made his dera in the new king's heart and now he seeks to replace Dhian Singh in the court. The Dogra has been denied access into the royal zenana, an access that he enjoyed during the old Lion's time.

The factions have formed. Dhian Singh and his brothers, the respected Bhais, the noble Attariwala and Sandhawalia Sardars have forgotten their own differences and together they seek to turn Naunihal against his own father. Bring back the glory of your grandfather, they appeal to him. Your father and his advisers will lead us all to ruin. Naunihal holds durbar twice a day in his haveli . . . his father is lost in religious discourse when he is not out of his senses with opium and the love of the young Bajwa.

It is not said, but Shah Mohammed knows: Naunihal has appealed to his father. Give up Chet Singh, but the Maharaja is adamant. Take lands, horses, elephants, he says, but do not ask me to do this. He has also refused Naunihal the twenty-lakh jagir that he wanted—the entire Doaba. Take lands on both sides of the Ravi instead, the Maharaja has offered.

O Shah Mohammed, soon there may be none to give the land, and none to take.

And then, barely three months after we had left Lahore in our palanquins, the missive came that chilled our hearts:

Katak, the first day.

Blood flows down the slopes of the fort. And more will flow. The swords have come out in the night. Now there is only one end.

Naunihal Singh, Dhian Singh and his brothers, Ajit Singh Sandhawalia and some others went into the fort after the darkest hour of the night. They entered the safest of safe places, the khwabgah of the Maharaja, where even dreams hesitate to go. All doors opened quietly for them. They pulled the trembling Chet Singh Bajwa out of the Maharaja's arms and stabbed him in the heart. Nobody is sure who raised his dagger first, but the name of Dhian Singh, whom Bajwa had challenged in open court the same day, is commonly taken. He sprang like a tiger, they say, and plunged the dagger into Bajwa's heart, saying: 'Take this in the memory of Ranjit Singh.'

Maharaja Kharak Singh lost his dear friend, in front of his eyes. From his mouth a terrible curse fell upon the killers.

They would all die, he said—the Rajas of Jammu, the Sardars, even his own son. And the great kingdom shall come to nought.

Ranjit Singh's empire is cursed by his own son.

O Shah Mohammed, the hour is dark.

The cold days came sooner in Jammu than they used to in Lahore. They reminded me of my own home in Kangra, and my parents— yes, even the father who sold me, for he did love me; he wasn't strong enough to defy fate and hunger, that is all. I was reminded of my younger brother Manglu. I feared for him. The two of us had shared many dark, hungry days. Even those who share their food have a special bond between them, but those who share hunger are bound till the next world. If only I could get word across to him, if only he was still at home and had not been sold to some unknown traveller, gone from hand to hand and finally to some house in Delhi or Agra, I could help him. I could always ask Rani Jindan to put in a word with Raja Suchet Singh to give Manglu a good job, in the stables or in the kennels or in the armoury.

But I did nothing. The greed and selfishness, the khudgarzi that destroys empires and has soaked our history in blood is not the disease only of kings and princes and ambitious ranis. We are all sick with it—even people like you and I, Arur, in small ways, maybe, but we are. I would not leave the life I had found, the new family—of a rani and a prince—that I had found, to go in search of my little brother. I would only carry the pain and shed some tears for him

sometimes and feel cleansed, like a saint . . . And I can then forgive
Dula ji the things you say he did in his last years. That sickness of the
self can even break the gods, and he was only a man; he was even
without the cloak of kingship under which so much wrong and
failure can be hidden away. Did not the Sarkar, his father, make
mistakes and compromises? But who remembers those? Success and
power make virtue of vice. I have things to say to the world, Arur,
to those who attack Duleep, people whom life hasn't tested . . . But
look at me, jabbering on about things you know better than me . . .

So there we were in Jammu, and we continued to pass our days
in that cold haveli that faced the brunt of the icy winds from the Pir
Panjal mountains. I had heard those mountains were so high that
one could not see their tops and there was always snow on them. In
the early morning, there used to be a thin frost right there, on the
brown grass outside the haveli. The Tawi became narrow, cold and
blue, and one could see much of the deep opposite bank that ran up
to the gate of the fort.

On winter afternoons, we girls sat around Jindan in the sunny
courtyard, busy with our weaving and our embroidery, watching
Duleep as he stumbled around after his pet parrots. Almost every
day the merchants from the bazaar would line up, the ones who
brought the soft wool from Kashmir, or silk from Banaras, or
coloured threads of every shade of the rainbow . . . Even the cold
days could be pleasant.

But the news from Lahore continued to worsen. The day we
received this letter from Shah Mohammed, our hearts were heavy
with sorrow:

Maghar, the fifth day.

*I fear to look towards Summan Burj these days. It is deserted,
haunted. Everything still happens, the durbars, the parades, the goings
and comings, but the spirit has gone. O noble Sarkar, never did Punjab
realize how much you meant. These days in Summan Burj there is only
mistrust, fear, rage and madness.*

*Maharaja or prisoner, Kharak Singh walks alone in those rooms,
banging his head against doors, grieving for his beloved Chet Singh. He*

does not trust his son, he openly rails against Dhian Singh, but his word
does not carry any meaning. Neither Kanwar Naunihal nor Dhian
Singh listen to him; Punjab wastes away without a real king.

In frustration, Kharak Singh mounted his horse one night and,
taking two sowars with him, rode out of the fort, galloping across the
plain. Naunihal and some trusted men rushed after him. Near
Sheikhupura, they held his bridle and turned him back and forced him
back on the gaddi. I do not know whose pain is greater, that of ordinary
prisoners or of a prisoner who is also a king.

The firanghi is watching and he is not idle. He is nibbling at the
kingdom. Today the redcoat army is allowed passage through Punjab on
their way to Kabul, tomorrow they will march on our heads.

Naunihal and Dhian Singh are allies only in name. The young Sikh
prince is only nineteen years of age, his shadow is not large enough to
take in the Dogra. Already there is talk that they will replace each
other's men, that the Kanwar will remove Dhian Singh from the post of
deodhidar, by virtue of which he has controlled access to the throne for
so many years. Dhian Singh feels the insult. He hardly goes to the
durbar. Instead, he prefers to go for shikar.

The riders began to arrive when the first snow fell on the higher
reaches around the town. I saw two of them in the bazaar chowk,
with their carbines and swords. They were Raja Dhian Singh's
soldiers. Later the same afternoon we saw some more riding into the
fort.

'What is happening, Mangla?' Jindan asked me when she looked
across the river and saw the gates of the mud fort open and swallow
the riders. She had this belief that I knew everything. Well, that was
my way. Either I knew, or I pretended to know, or I found out. The
news was not difficult to get. Dhian Singh was expected to come
back to Jammu any time. He was retiring from Lahore. The insults
had piled up until he could not tolerate it any more.

'But how will the work of the durbar continue without him?'
Jindan's forehead was creased with genuine concern.

'They will have to find some way, Rani ji. There are many other
wise men there,' I said to reassure her.

Meanwhile, Raja Dhian Singh's soldiers began to take over the town. They could be seen at every chowk, in groups of four or five, gossiping, laughing, jousting with each other. And as their number increased so did the stories about Lahore. The English agent in Ludhiana, Colonel Wade, a great friend of Kharak Singh, had been removed and a new man named Clerk was to take over. Kharak Singh was indisposed, still grieving for Chet Singh Bajwa and those who were looking after him were rumoured to be giving him a slow poison with his food. Some said it was safed kasturi, others said it was kamphoor ras, or maybe both. Yet others said these rumours were malicious: Naunihal Singh was a dutiful son and many physicians had been sent to look after his father.

The gifts arrived early in the morning. Five thaals of sweets, five baskets of fresh fruits—shining apples and grapes from Kabul, Kandahari pomegranates—and five more thaals heaped with dry fruits—raisins, shelled walnuts, large pistachio. I had been waiting for this. Raja Dhian Singh had been in Jammu for a week and it was known that sooner or later, he would come to see Jindan. In Lahore, he was a frequent visitor to the zenana, as was his son, Hira Singh. In fact, Hira Singh was almost brought up in the zenana, spending the afternoons there, joking and playing with our Sarkar. Every night the Sarkar put five hundred rupees near his pillow, which Hira Singh was supposed to give away to the poor in the morning. Of course he never gave away anything . . .

But in those days Dhian Singh had never had a conversation with Jindan. He used to talk to some of the senior maharanis, those whom he had known longer or those whom he thought to be more important.

'Stay close, Mangla,' she said thoughtfully now. 'I wonder what he will propose.'

She decided to receive him in the large room beyond the veranda. It was a comfortable room where we often sat in the evenings, when the courtyard was too cold and talk still on our minds. The room had been warmed by an angithi with red-hot coals and its floor was covered with thick rugs. Rani Jindan sat on a couch warmed by woollen shawls, an embroidered cushion under her arm. Duleep lay asleep in a cradle near her, a cradle built for him from hard shisham, polished until it was a dark deep brown and embellished with gold paint. Silver trays of sweetmeats and dry fruits had been set out for the guests and the incense rising from the lamp in the corner made the whole room very pleasant.

As soon as I heard the horses on the stone path that led up to the haveli, I moved into the shadows, behind one of the three pillars. From here I would be able to hear and see everything and in case the Rani needed me, I would be present immediately.

I heard Raja Dhian Singh clear his throat at the door and enter the room. I could see him clearly through the thin veil of my dupatta. I had never seen him so close. In the Sarkar's time he was a very important person; the second most powerful in all of Punjab. A slave like me had little chance of being up close in his presence. I had seen him riding once, a handsome, regal presence. I had seen him on one or two occasions in the durbar, including the day that my fate had been decided and I was assigned to Rani Jindan. That day he had stood behind the Sarkar, listening politely, his hands folded in front of him. He had bent down once or twice to say something in the Maharaja's ear.

I watched him closely. He could not have been much over thirty. He moved with a slight limp to the centre of the room. I dared to look at his face and was astounded by the sharpness of his features. He had a neat beard and moustache and a small white turban. He wore a quilted shirt of green silk and a jacket of soft wool over it. Around his neck were several necklaces of pearls.

'Sat Sri Akal, Rani ji, thank you for receiving this old faithful servant of the Sarkar.' His voice was soft and silky, his tone very polite.

Jindan was silent for a brief moment and then the self-assuredness of her reply surprised me. She spoke as if she had been born to be a queen. 'You are welcome, Raja-e-Rajgan. Anybody who has served the Sarkar and Punjab like you have is always welcome. What brings you away from the durbar?'

'Bad days, Rani ji, terrible times. Wisdom has flown with the spirit of the Sarkar. It pains my heart to even think of these things. With what pain, with what self-sacrifice had Sarkar built this kingdom, brick by brick, inspired by the teachings of the Gurus, armed with the bravery of the Khalsa.'

'I have heard of some of the goings-on at the durbar but did not think that you would ever leave.'

'The times dictated it, Rani ji. My heart is still there. My spirit pines to give my best to the kingdom, even my life. I wish I had been allowed to burn on the Sarkar's pyre.'

'God forbid. The kingdom needs you.'

'It does not seem like it, Rani ji. Maharaja Kharak Singh does not trust me, though I swore my faith on the dead body of our Sarkar. And Naunihal is again misled by those who would rather have me away. The Sarkar did not distinguish between Sikh and Dogra, but these things have become important now. But let us leave all that aside, I only came to ask after your welfare. I trust Jammu has looked after you well.'

'It has given us solace in a difficult time.'

'All that I have, all that my brothers have, is at your disposal. And the young prince, I trust that he grows well.'

'With Waheguru's grace.'

She glanced towards the cradle. I saw Raja Dhian Singh move towards it. He bent down over the sleeping Duleep with folded hands.

'He sleeps with such dignity, such peace. May Waheguru grant him a long and happy life.'

Just then the child stirred and opened his eyes. Dhian Singh reached into his jacket and took out a gold chain. I could see an emerald pendant shining in his palm as he held it out for the Rani to see.

'Allow me, Rani ji, to offer this small nazrana to this youngest scion of our beloved Sarkar.'

Gently he took the child's hand and putting the chain in the tiny palm closed the fingers over it.

'You are kind, Raja ji. He is just a child, far away from the throne.'

Then Dhian Singh spoke in a more serious tone.

'Please take care of him. We all must take care of him. He may not remain so far away from the throne for too long. When the time is right, we will call you back to Lahore.'

'What did he mean, Mangla?' Jindan asked me when he had finally left and the sound of the hooves had died in the distance.

'I do not understand, Rani ji. Perhaps he knows more than we do.'

She smiled slowly. Perhaps she understood more than what she wanted to show.

But Dhian Singh was a mere mortal. Even God could not have known what was to follow. Things like that do not happen very often in history. Search through your great books, here and across the oceans. Ask poets and wise men, if you want. Such storms, driven by the most evil spirits, bloodthirsty, avenging spirits, come when a deep misfortune falls over a land and human beings become like motes of dust, blown this way or that, some swept to their destiny, others to their death.

The sulking Dhian Singh was soon called back to Lahore. Naunihal Singh could not do without him, the work of the durbar had come to a standstill. Even Dhian Singh's enemies had to recognize his talents. Victorious and laughing, his soldiers began to ride back, rested in body and spirit, their weapons sharp and glistening.

Before he left, the Raja once again came to see Jindan. Again he mentioned the possibility of our return to Lahore.

'My humble haveli in Chuna Mandi shall be your home, Rani ji. And the home of our young prince Duleep. There he will be taken care of as future kings are. And he will be close to the throne and yet safe.'

Katak, the twenty-ninth day.

Maharaja Kharak Singh's eternal curse on his own kingdom, the cries of a heart-sick lover, the tears of a king, prisoner in his own fort, the yearning of a father to see his only son before his death . . . all these have risen to the heavens.

And in the heavens they have been heard.

Nothing else explains the questions that are being screamed out in all directions from the towers of Lahore fort, the screams that are renting the palace walls as if they were made not of stone but of silk as delicate as a mother's heart, the tears that are in every eye, Hindu, Sikh, Musalman.

This year Diwali fell on a Saturday. Such years are heavy on kings and queens, on armies and nobles, on courts and palaces. Kharak Singh Sarkar barely survived the Diwali celebrations in Amritsar but the journey back to Lahore proved too much for him. He has passed on but he was known to be a guest of a few days anyway. Either his illness got him, or as the people in the bazaar say, it was the kamphoor ras and safed kasturi being mixed in his wine at the behest of Dhian Singh and Naunihal. I do not believe these rumours. But then I do not believe anything spoken by a human tongue. There are some who say that Naunihal was ambitious but he was not a murderer. He cried like a true son when he saw his dead father, they say, and that Kharak Singh died of a disease that kills the weak: a broken heart—he was tired of battling the Dogras, tired of thinking why his son sided with them even though he hated them, tired of mourning for Chet Singh Bajwa.

Ishar Kaur Maharani became sati. Her beauty used to be the talk of Sialkot, and even on her last day, she was beautiful. Daughter of Sandhu Sardars, she should not have become sati. There are rumours that Raja Dhian Singh forced her to burn with the Maharaja. She knew too much, her niece was married to Chet Singh Bajwa. Maharani Chand Kaur, the elder Maharani of Kharak Singh and mother of Naunihal, did not reach Lahore.

Thousands had gathered outside Roshni darwaza to watch Ishar Kaur and eleven of her pitiful slaves burn with the Maharaja on the royal pyre. With folded hands Dhian Singh approached the sati queen: 'Mai ji, pray for the long life of Kanwar Naunihal, for the eternal victory of the kingdom of Maharaja Ranjit Singh.'

Mai Ishar Kaur answered with a frown, 'Each one of us must harvest what we sow.'

She sat down on the pyre and put the head of the Maharaja on her thigh.

'Please, with your own hands, Mai ji, give us the kalgi of the Sarkar, it shall adorn the Kanwar's head, it shall be a blessing for his life, a charm for his rule.'

'There is nothing in the kalgi,' said the angry Rani, 'it is all in the will of the Almighty.'

And she threw down the plume from Kharak Singh's turban on the earth and was consumed by the fire lit by Naunihal. And now there are people who whisper: 'Those who become sati by their own will are blessed, at least in their own eyes. But those who are forced at the point of the sword, leave behind only curses.'

The sun was already up in the sky and though it was the month of Katak, the day suddenly turned hot. Naunihal stood by the burning pyre until he could stand no more. He was overwhelmed by grief, perhaps, or the heat, or the smell of burning flesh. Quickly the attendants led him away. A few yards away he stopped and holding his stomach, he vomited, twice. The pyre was forgotten, all attention turned to the young Kanwar. He was led away to the Sarkar's samadh. In its shade, he rested against the wall. Two attendants wiped his brow and fanned him. Someone gave him a cool drink of gulab sherbet that takes away the heat from the head. Then it was time to join the mourners to bathe so that all could wash off the smoke of the cremation from their bodies and go home. He began to walk towards the nullah that flows along the wall of the fort down to the Ravi. There isn't too much water there in these winter months, hardly enough to stand in and bathe. His ablutions done, Naunihal raised his folded hands to the cloudless skies and prayed for the soul of his departed father. His step, as he moved out of the water, was heavy. That was only inevitable. No matter how brave the man, how tough of heart, no matter if he is twenty or sixty, a father's death is difficult to bear. A father's death leaves one open to the heavens, there is no protection any more. The burden could already be seen in the bent of Naunihal's shoulders as he put a hand on his thigh and climbed up the slope.

Mian Udham Singh, son of Raja Gulab Singh, his dear friend of childhood days, came up to hug the Kanwar. In the hour of grief, minor differences and political agendas are quickly forgotten, humbled before the Great Giver. Naunihal threw his arm over Udham's shoulder and together they walked from the nullah towards Roshni darwaza. Together they entered the old archway of the Mughals. But destiny had not yet played out her full hand. The sad day was yet to do its worst. That archway, which perhaps had been waiting for centuries to choose the saddest moment to fall, it fell then, as the young prince and his companion passed under it.

There was chaos everywhere. Stone and brick, mortar and lime fell on the young royal head and that of his companion. The horses standing near the stone steps reared up, the elephants quickly stepped backwards, *nearly throwing off their mahouts, their trunks swinging wildly in fear. Screams rose from the walls of the fort where people had lined up to see the cremation. Little did they know that before one cremation was over, nature was preparing another pyre.*

Udham Singh was dead, killed on the spot under the ancient stones. Naunihal was unconscious. They took him away to the baradari in Hazuribagh, shutting the gates behind them. Dhian Singh drove away all who tarried. There where his grandfather used to hold court, there where happiness used to rule not so long ago, the young prince lay, dying. Or dead. Nobody knew. Only in the late evening, when the Kanwar was taken inside the fort in a heavily guarded palki, did the gate to Hazuribagh open. Like so many others, I went and stood beside it. The first rumour came after the last peher of the night had passed, with the horses that rode out of the fort in groups of four. A rider shouted that they were away on the road to Kahnwan and the rest I could surmise. That was where Sher Singh was. The horses were going in fours to set up stages for him to return speedily. The Kanwar must be dead.

And so it was. In two days' time, after Sher Singh entered the fort, having ridden day and night, the sad news was given out. A tired Lahore shed tears again and all else—the river, the ancient stones, the lowering skies—began to mourn when another pyre, that of a young man who should have ruled many years, who at the age of thirteen had gone to conquer Peshawar, a warrior trained by the brave Hari Singh Nalwa, was prepared. Two more young queens got ready for sati.

There is of course much more to write.

Who knows how that archway fell?

Did it fall from old age, weakened by the sound of cannons that were fired from the walls to announce Kharak Singh's cremation, cannons that shook even the walls of my house down in the city? Or had Raja Dhian Singh hatched a plan to finish Ranjit Singh's lineage in one day and clear the way for his lifelong wazirat and the rule of his own son Hira Singh on the throne of Punjab? Or was it justice done by the Great Giver who sees everything from his throne in the sky?

There are as many stories as there are tongues in these lanes.

But I do not have the heart any more to write, or the desire. I was to write to you the gossip of the palace, of pleasant goings-on, of royal guests and celebrations. I was to write of prosperity and victories of the Khalsa. I have already written too much of death. And yet, I know, there is more.

I could understand what Shah Mohammed felt. All our hearts were heavy and no one knew what would happen next. Rani Jindan sat for many days in deep thought, as if she was weighing one option against another, moving chess pieces in her mind. At night, she would no longer let Duleep sleep in his shisham cradle. She would insist that I put him in her own bed, cover him with her own satin quilt. Often at night she would hold the prince's face in both her hands and look at it long and fondly, as if she was trying to fix it forever in her memory.

Those were dark days, full of fear and anxiety as our Punjab fell apart. Despite his grief Shah Mohammed wrote again:

Poh, the last day.

Allah is angry with our Punjab. He shook the earth so hard that two of the cupolas of Badshahi Masjid fell to the ground far below and people cowered in doorways, waiting for the earth to be still again. The kingdom is fatherless, anybody can reach for the throne. Sher Singh is the eldest of the surviving princes. His claim is the strongest. His twin Tara Singh is of course an imbecile; the others—Peshaura, Kashmira, Multana and Duleep are too young. But Chand Kaur, Naunihal's mother and Kharak Singh's queen, I hear, will not allow that. She has staked a claim on behalf of Naunihal's unborn child.

Everything hangs in an uneasy balance as the rivals wait for Naunihal's child to be born. Chand Kaur is the regent in the palace; Sher Singh bides his time in Batala. But thrones do not wait. Confusion has begun to rule. Meanwhile, the Dogra brothers pretend to have parted ways. Gulab Singh will aid Chand Kaur while Dhian Singh is with Sher Singh.

One day, with three hundred horsemen, Sher Singh sets up camp at Budhu Ka Ava in a house atop a mound of burnt bricks. A huge roar from his supporters rises into the sky: 'Sher Singh Badshah! Dhian Singh Wazir!' And far away, Chand Kaur, Gulab Singh and the other

Sardars in the fort hear the roar and watch the campfires of the besiegers light up all the way to the horizon on the plains of Mian Mir.

The defenders of the fort make hasty preparations. Every gate is armed, every man paid and loaded muskets glint from the portholes and the ramparts. Gulab Singh rides in every direction, exhorting his troops to fight to the finish. But mere oaths do not always work. So both sides begin to buy up the Khalsa battalions. In twenty-four hours three lakh rupees are distributed by Gulab Singh and five lakh by Sher Singh.

The gates of the city readily admit Sher Singh and his troops. The soldiers loot and plunder and the townspeople huddle in misery, cold and hungry, caught in the crossfire. Fourteen guns blast down the Akbari darwaza and marksmen from atop the minarets of Badshahi Masjid fire into the fort. But the defenders return the fire and Hazuribagh is soon strewn with the Khalsa dead. Day and night the guns continue to fire, the walls of the fort are breached in many places and yet there is no sign of surrender.

Finally, Dhian Singh arrives and the two Dogra brothers negotiate a peace. Chand Kaur will retire with a personal allowance of twenty lakh rupees a year. And on Basant Panchami 1841, Sher Singh enters Lahore fort to take his place on the throne. Gulab Singh makes his peace with the new Maharaja by presenting him the Koh-i-noor.

Now the guns have fallen silent, the dead have been cremated and the breaches in the walls of the fort repaired. But the lull can only be temporary.

Naunihal's young queen delivered a stillborn child and died in the process. And slave girls killed Chand Kaur as she lay in her bath. Sher Singh's hand? Dhian Singh's? Gulab Singh's? Perhaps, yes to each, or all; and perhaps, no.

The Khalsa soldiers watched with mounting anger. They had not got the pay raises promised to them in the heat of battle. Munshis and clerks who kept tabs on payments to the army were pulled out of their houses to swear allegiance to the Khalsa; the worst of them were simply finished off with a lunge of the lance or a swift chop of the sword. The Khalsa army has learnt that no one can rule Lahore without them, and they will make that count. They don't like much else that goes on in the palace. Not the dominance of the Dogras, nor the debauchery of the

Sardars. Ranjit Singh had always consulted them, carried them with him. He had the stomach and the head to keep them loyal to him and in awe of him. None of the rivals to the throne now command that kind of confidence.

And the firanghi is watching, from across the Sutlej. Both Sher Singh and Chand Kaur had made overtures to the British for support of their rival claims. The firanghis know that sovereignty may be for sale in Punjab. They can afford to wait it out . . . In the meantime, I hear that your young prince has become an object of interest to them.

In Jammu, we were spared the terrors visiting Lahore. Summer became winter and then it was summer again. My dear Duleep began to speak. I loved his prattle. I taught him his first words— Pani, Bibi, Mai . . . I did not know then that he would go away so far, Vilayat, Rus, and God knows where else, learn all those languages, cross swords with Englishmen in their courts and newspapers. I remember the first time he said Bibi, Jindan's eyes lit up as if with a thousand candles and she distributed a hundred and one silver coins among the girls! After that, all the girls would want to be the first one to tell her of any new word that Duleep spoke and be rewarded.

Young Suchet Singh became a regular visitor from Lahore. He would always bring nice gifts, for Rani Jindan and for the girls, especially for me. He knew that I was the closest to her, that if he really wanted to tell her something, all he had to do was to tell me and the job would be done. I collected many beautiful trinkets those days, necklaces, earrings, noserings. He had more where all that came from; his treasures were legend. When he died, they found that he had buried it all somewhere in British territory.

The handsome Raja would spend long hours with Jindan and it would warm my heart to hear her laughing freely. That laughter captivated him; he would keep looking at her face when she laughed like that. On those evenings, the girls would sing and dance before them and our haveli would once again seem like the royal house it should have been. When he came, so did his charyaari riders, including Mian Devi Singh. He was especially close to Suchet Singh and would not let him out of his sight even for a minute. It was my job to take care of him, ensure that he got good food and drink and rest. It was a pleasant task. Devi Singh was a swaggering, tall man, a real soldier who smelt of battle and horses. When, after he had had three or four goblets of wine, he would look into my eyes, I would forget that I was just an ordinary girl from the hills. And I would pester him for news of Lahore, fragments of gossip and intrigue, the rumours of the bazaar, the goings-on in Summan Burj. When he talked I would shut my eyes and think that I was actually back in Lahore, breathing its fragrant winds, watching from my window the white domes across the Ravi, where Jahangir and his beautiful empress Noor Jahan lay buried under marble.

'You are better off here,' he told me one day, as he rested after dinner against his favourite round pillows. 'In Lahore nowadays maidservants are up against difficult times. You know what happened to the four maidservants of Rani Chand Kaur who killed her? Their hands, their noses and ears were chopped off in the square outside the kotwali and they were turned out of the city.'

I gasped.

'Was a girl called Heero Ganji among them? A girl with very fine features but dark complexion, my height, thin?'

'I don't remember the names but one of them did look like you describe. They deserved it, they were clumsy. They couldn't kill her with poison in her gulab arq. So the stupid girls smashed her head with stones as they bathed her, but they couldn't even manage *that* well! In the three days it took her to die, the whole city knew some evil was afoot.'

'But you can tell me the actual truth,' I cajoled Devi Singh into telling me more.

'Of course. Sher Singh gave the signal to Raja Dhian Singh and left for Wazirabad. And Dhian Singh found his instruments through the thanedar of Lahore. That was all. Four slave girls across the river and Chand Kaur out of the way. But why talk of maids and slave girls, the times are not good for us either.'

I poured more wine into his glass and he smiled appreciatively, running his fingers through my hair. I begged him to continue.

'These days, the durbar belongs to the Sardars and there is a cloud over the three Jammu Rajas and their faithfuls like me. That is why we have come away. Sher Singh is again in the hands of the Sandhawalias and spends his days drinking and hunting with them. He has forgotten that they plotted against him and helped Chand Kaur.'

'But surely,' I said, 'Raja Dhian Singh will advise him against them.'

'Sher Singh does not listen to him any longer. He has let in snakes and will pay the price.'

That summer Dhian Singh again left Lahore in disgust. Very soon the work of the durbar came to a standstill. Messengers were sent to Jammu to fetch him. Ultimately a firman had to be issued, commanding the Raja to return to the durbar, explain his work for the last five years and to present his accounts to Maharaja Sher Singh. In all his wisdom and on the advice of his brothers, Dhian Singh went back to Lahore.

But before he went, he sent a message to Rani Jindan, telling her that she should prepare to return to Lahore with prince Duleep Singh.

The time had come.

We did not go together to Lahore. Jindan was far too clever for that. We knew that things there might not be very safe for the Rani or for Duleep. Even Sher Singh feared for his life and spent days away, on horseback, hunting and hawking. Nobody knew where the Raj lay any more—in the fort or in the streets, with Wazir Dhian Singh or with the Khalsa army with its powerful Panch Sardars.

No. Lahore was not the place it used to be.

So Rani Jindan went first. Before she left, she called me into her room and gave me a pashmina doshala and a full new set of ornaments—a two-string pearl necklace, bangles, earrings, panjebs, everything.

'You have to take care of my son, Mangla. Hold him dearer than your own life. I would take him with me, but I am not certain of what awaits me. If all is well, we will soon be together.'

We didn't have to wait too long. In a few weeks the message came that we could follow. All those who mattered had begged for the return of Duleep to the city of his father.

So once again I set out for the lanes and bazaars that I loved so much. During the four-day journey, I hardly slept, and never let Duleep out of my sight.

Excitement rippled through our haveli that morning. Everybody, from the Rani to the bhaiyyas who stood in the outer courtyard to convey messages or fetch and carry things, felt that excitement. And I of course had been the first to get the news. A khidmatgar from Raja Dhian Singh's haveli had come early in the morning, an old and trusted man whose name I now forget but whose face is clear in my mind even after so many years.

'When the day is four hours gone,' he said, 'Raja sahib will come to meet your mistress. I have been asked to convey that besides him, there will be his precious son, Hira Singh and his brother, Suchet Singh. The Sandhawalia Sardars have also been invited. Shahzada Duleep Singh is expected to receive them all.'

I ran inside and told Rani Jindan what to expect. She was pacing back and forth in her chamber, lost in thought. I understood what was bothering her. The Jammu Rajas and the Sandhawalia Sardars were sworn enemies. What was it that they had to discuss in her house and what were they planning for her son, a child of barely five years?

'Get the child ready, Mangla,' she finally said. 'Dress him as if he was going to the durbar and make him wear his turban and all his jewels.'

I had been waiting for such a day. I woke up the young prince, bathed him, combed his beautiful long hair and dressed him up. When he was ready I called in the mirror bearer. When he saw himself in the mirror, the dear child turned to look at me and smiled. My heart stopped beating with the joy that his smile filled me with, and with a strange, fierce foreboding. I lived with a nameless fear ever afterwards . . .

The Jammu Rajas arrived first on their elephants. Dhian Singh descended from his silver howdah and, leaving his soldiers at the door of the haveli, proceeded to the large hall in which Jindan was waiting. Hira Singh and Suchet Singh came on another elephant and followed him inside. I had heard so much about Hira Singh, of his good looks, of his closeness to the noble Ranjit Singh. He alone, besides the Sarkar's own sons, could sit in a chair in the durbar and he alone had the courage to interrupt the Sarkar or speak without being asked to. That was the first day I saw him in flesh and blood. He looked fit to sit on a throne himself. Something about him made me fear for Duleep even more. What did men like him and the Sardars want from a mere child?

The Sardars came almost immediately after, galloping on their beautifully decorated horses.

'Sat Sri Akal!' they shouted, as they jumped off their horses and threw the reins to their khidmatgars.

Ajit Singh was one of the original char yaar, handsome as ever but his jowls were beginning to thicken and his shoulders had rounded. His uncle Lehna Singh was older and taller. His bristling beard covered his dark cheeks. Just to look at him made me gasp, such was the fire in his eyes.

They all did a sirwarna of Duleep. The Nanakshahi coins they waved round his head kept coming into my hands as I stood behind Jindan. There were presents too: heron plumes for his turban, encrusted with precious stones, rings, a string of pearls. We served gulab sherbet and sweets and then the servants withdrew. I too walked towards the door but with a look of her blessed eyes Rani Jindan asked me to stay. I moved to a corner. I had learnt to stand still on such occasions, as if I was a pillar of stone. It was a useful trick; people barely noticed I was there at all.

'You are welcome back in Lahore, Rani ji,' Dhian Singh began. 'I know I can speak for all of us to wish the Shahzada a long life and assure you of our services and support through good days and difficult ones.'

'I agree,' Ajit Singh Sandhawalia spoke up. 'Our hearts are full of honour and love for the young prince. Our heads are bowed with the many favours the noble Sarkar bestowed on us and we wait only for a chance to return those favours, even with our lives.'

Jindan did not say anything but waited for Dhian Singh to continue.

'The last few months have not been easy. We have stood by Maharaja Sher Singh but we do not know where we are headed. The ship of our kingdom is sailing in turbulent waters and the Maharaja is indifferent. I have tried my best but I am only a Wazir, not a king.'

The Sandhawalia Sardars held their silence. The last few months had been good for them. After first siding with Chand Kaur, they had somehow managed to find favour with Sher Singh. Ajit Singh had been presented with sixteen robes of honour, a horse with a gold harness and a sword. His uncle too, who now sat next to him, his body tall and straight, his bloodshot eyes looking straight at one speaker then another, had been released from Mukerian prison and rewarded in the same manner. Only the eldest Sandhawalia Sardar, the noble Attar Singh, still waited at Una for an honourable return home.

'We have tried our best that the Maharaja should give up his love of shikar and take the reins of the durbar in his own hands,' continued Dhian Singh. 'But we have failed.'

Lehna Singh then spoke up, abruptly.

'There is no need to mince words when we are in such a situation. Let me speak directly, as a simple soldier. We may have had our differences with Raja Dhian Singh in the past but we know he is a wise Wazir and has served the state long and well. We are willing to throw our weight behind him and help him change our leader now. Shahzada Duleep Singh should sit on the throne of Punjab and we are ready to shed our last drop of blood for that.'

As he spoke, I could see his hand on his sword and the glistening blade was already half out of its scabbard. I saw Jindan's hand reach towards Duleep.

'He is too young. He does not understand any of this.'

'That is why we are here, Rani ji,' the young Hira Singh spoke for the first time. 'Our family has always served the throne faithfully. We will serve Duleep Singh too.'

I saw Lehna Singh's eyes rest on Hira Singh. There was poison in that look. He made to say something but Ajit Singh put a hand on his arm and he stayed quiet.

I could not stand there any longer. My legs were refusing to support me. On the pretext of refilling the goblets of sherbet, I slipped out of the room. My heart was pounding in my breast with the sound of a hundred horses. What strange destiny could lead a five-year-old to the throne? And what strange destiny was pushing me, poor Piru Mal's daughter, to be part of all this? I sat down on the steps of the courtyard, waiting for my heart to calm down. I could see the fort and the high Summan Burj, sombre against a rain-laden sky. A flag still flew there. Sher Singh was still alive, and still very much the Maharaja.

The clouds that had been threatening us for so many days finally broke and the warm rain came thrashing down on the city and the fort and the surrounding plains. Such rain, after the long summer, was always a relief; one could breathe again. Near the bank of the Ravi, away from the walls of the fort, the peacocks sang, arching their silken blue necks towards the grey sky. In the lanes naked children played like the peacocks, welcoming the rain with open arms, splashing in the puddles. And sometimes we could even hear the elephants trumpeting happily.

But the rain did not last long enough and when it stopped, an oppressive heat once again settled on us. The sun that came up was a vicious one, as if it wanted to settle scores for all the cloudy, sunless days that had come our way. Not a breath of wind filtered into the lanes of Lahore and our arms ached with fanning ourselves. We took turns among the girls to fan Rani Jindan and Duleep as he slept in the cool chamber of the haveli. On one such silent, sleepy afternoon, an exciting whisper raced through the lanes.

'He has gone mad, that old ghorcharha rider. He has lost his head!'

The ghorcharha riders were always a little mad. Ruffians all of them, unlike the regular troops who had been put together by the Sarkar's firanghi jarnails. Ghorcharhas did not wear identical uniforms, nor did they carry the same weapons. And of course they had never been seen standing in a straight line. They were united only in their destiny as warriors, in their desire to taste victory after victory. These adventurers rode without fear, as if with their heads on their outstretched palms, available for the taking only if someone dared. And when they rode, they saw neither light nor dark, night nor day. They would rise from their dera at dawn, gather for their prayers with the granthi while it was still dark and then quickly

brushing their long beards and tying their quoit turbans they would
be in the saddle, heading for whatever campaign possessed them at
that moment.

These mad riders were the Sarkar's special soldiers—
unpredictable, uncontrollable, unbeatable. They had helped him
beat other misls into submission. Those had been their glory days.

'Come on, Mangla,' the young girls beseeched me. 'Let us go
and see him. They say that under the spell of his bhang he is saying
all sorts of strange things.'

To tell the truth, I was curious too. I half led, half followed the
excited girls out of the haveli and towards the chowk of Tripolia
bazaar.

The man had a long lance in his right hand. His small round
shield shone in the other. His face was set as if he had nothing to
lose. He was not a young man, his beard was grey and wrinkles
covered his sun-beaten face.

'Take away my horse, take away my sword!' he raged. 'But you
cannot take away the spirit that the Guru has given me, with his own
hand!'

He whirled around with the lance outstretched in one hand,
creating a circle around him as people shrank back from the point
of his weapon.

'What happened?' I asked of no one in particular.

Someone in the crowd responded.

'This morning Maharaja Sher Singh threw him out of the
parade. Told him to go home, retire. Told him that he is too old. He
is heartbroken.'

There were still ghorcharhas in service who belonged not only to
the time of Ranjit Singh but also that of his father Maha Singh
Sukerchekia. They may not have been able to fight any longer but
they could not be asked to go home. They had given their lives and
their blood for our army.

'Go home, they tell me, and till the land!' the old rider was
shouting. 'Go home to what? My home is my saddle, my sword has
mown only the heads of ghazis. I have fought at the forts of Kangra
and Jammu; I have seen Multan and Kashmir fall at my feet. All for
my Sarkar. And now he tells me, this illegitimate son of a dyer who

has grabbed the great Sarkar's throne, that I should go home and farm? Never!'

The crowd had grown thick and on hearing the Maharaja spoken of in these terms, a hush fell over them. The old soldier was risking his life with each word he said. Any moment, I thought, he would be led away in chains to the fort. Or just beheaded before our very eyes.

But nothing happened. The ghorcharha raved and ranted for a while. Then he pointed towards his grey-and-white stallion that stood pawing the ground in his impatience.

'Take him, whoever wants. Pay me what you want. He is the wind itself. He has floated over ghazi armies like a venomous cloud.'

Immediately there were bids for the horse. The ghorcharha heard them and pointed out to a young man.

'Take him, my young hawk. You deserve him, and you have bid like a true soldier.'

Then still mumbling, the soldier settled down against an old stone wall. He took out some bhang from an inner pocket in his tunic and began to grind it in a black stone bowl that he took out of a leather bag slung over his left shoulder. But instead of tossing the bhang into his mouth, he shouted again, holding the bowl aloft in his left hand.

'Watch that tree. Watch what happens to that tree when this bhang hits it. The same fate will befall this kingdom!'

With a mighty heave he threw the bhang from his left hand at the trunk of a gnarled peepal that stood a few feet away. As soon as the bhang hit the bark, the tree seemed to get a life of its own. It rose out of the ground, roots and all, as if pulled by a hundred demons and fell many feet away on its side, its curled roots like a witch's claw. A gasp like a collective death-sigh, rose towards the sky. Nobody had ever seen anything like that and if I had not been there myself, I would never have believed it!

'That,' the man bellowed, one hand outstretched towards the fort, 'that is the way this kingdom will end. All of them will die. Kings and wazirs, Sardars and Dogras. This is the curse of a ghorcharha.'

A frenzy took over the city that night as the story of the

ghorcharha and the magic tree spread. Anybody who heard rushed to the place, pushing through the crowded lanes. People stared at the tree and said that evil days would now come upon the citizens.

In fact, that happened earlier than anyone could have expected.

It was the Sankrant of Asuj of the year forty-three. A sacred day, a day for giving charities and alms to the poor, a day for prayer. A sweet fresh breeze, cool with the promise of the coming winter blew through the courtyard of our haveli where I stood behind Duleep as he touched the money and the sacks of flour and rice that would be given away to the poor in his name. They were already lining up in the lane outside the haveli. In the last few weeks since the Dogra Rajas and the Sandhawalias had met at the haveli, word about the prince had spread fast across the city. Many important men had come to pay their respects to Rani Jindan and the prince. Dhian Singh himself had sent for Duleep more than once after that, sending him back each time on his own elephant, laden with gifts.

Suddenly the quiet of the morning was broken by the sound of hundreds of horses entering the city and riding towards the fort from the direction of Hazuribagh. It was unusual to hear so many riders coming into the fort, especially on Sankrant, a day when the durbar would not be held and Maharaja Sher Singh had been seen heading off towards the garden of Shah Bilawal, a few miles out of the city. Hardly had the sound of the galloping horses died down, than I heard gunfire. Two quick shots. And then silence. Quickly, I had the haveli gate shut and took Duleep indoors. Having made sure that he was safely inside with his mother, I stepped out again.

There was commotion afoot. People were leaving the bazaar and rushing indoors. Shops were being shut. I heard people shouting, passing on the news to each other.

'The Maharaja is dead! Sher Singh has been killed! Ajit Singh Sandhawalia has shot him.'

'The ghorcharha's prophecies will come true. God alone can protect us.'

'I've just met one of the soldiers who was in Shah Bilawal . . . Ajit Singh shot the Maharaja in the chest while showing him his new gun. In full view of everybody!'

'Even his young son Pratap has not been spared. Lehna Singh lopped off his head even as he was feeding the poor. How the boy begged for his life!'

I clapped my hands to my ears. Pratap Singh, Sher Singh's young son, a child, like Duleep!

The lanes were deserted as if a sudden plague had swept through them. Soon all I could see were barred windows and tightly shut doors. I too rushed back to the haveli but no sooner had I entered than a group of six soldiers rode up to the door and without any ceremony entered the haveli.

'We have come to guard the Shahzada,' they said. 'He is to be the Maharaja. This is the command of the Sandhawalias.'

'Sandhawalias?' the Rani managed to ask. 'What of the Wazir sahib, Raja Dhian Singh?'

One of the soldiers snorted. 'He got what was coming to him for a long time. The Sandhawalias shot him and cut him up. He's lying in bits in a ditch near the foundry.'

Before Rani Jindan or I could say a word, they entered the haveli and placed their guard around Duleep's chamber. My head was whirling with the news that I had heard. Such terrible killings and our young prince to sit on the throne of Punjab!

And then the drumbeaters were out in the streets. Mounted on a camel, the two men moved from mohalla to mohalla and at every chowk, they read out the proclamation that was to change our lives forever:

Punjab has new rulers. Duleep Singh will be the Maharaja, Lehna Singh Sandhawalia will be the Wazir. The kingdom is well rid of Maharaja Sher Singh, and the Raja Kalan Dhian Singh is dead. All the citizens of Lahore will be safe in the new dispensation. They should keep the peace, they have nothing to fear, they should continue their daily life and business . . .

Those were terrible days that followed, Arur. You are fortunate you were not born then. They were days of madness—bloodlust, revenge . . . Brutality and valour are very different things, but few remember this—the tragedy of all kingdoms as it was of Punjab.

The Sandhawalias had not won the day yet. Hira Singh and

Suchet Singh lost no time upon hearing of Dhian Singh's death. They rushed to the Khalsa troops to win them over. Hira Singh unbuckled his sword and held it out to the soldiers.

'My father, the great Wazir of Sarkar Ranjit Singh, has been killed today by traitors of Punjab. Use this sword and kill me too, or follow me to avenge the killing. The Sandhawalia traitors are in cahoots with the Angrez. If they win today, then it is only a matter of days before the firanghi redcoats cross the Sutlej by the thousand. That will be the end of Ranjit Singh's Punjab; that will be the end of the Khalsa army. All of you can give up your weapons and go home to till your lands.'

From Budhu Ka Ava to Anarkali, the young Dogra prince, darling of Ranjit Singh, rode from one cantonment to the other, firing the soldiers' blood with his speeches, whetting their appetites with visions of plunder and loot and promising them higher salaries. 'I will not eat till I kill my father's killers, and nor will my father's pyre be lit, and nor will his wife become sati.'

And what do the Khalsa troops need to go to battle? A higher salary and strong words. As the fifes and drums sounded, the soldiers left their evening meals half cooked and marched across the plain towards the city, prepared for a long night of vengeance. They came from all directions, their weapons at the ready, their cannon rolling with them, from Mian Mir, from Shahdara, from Anarkali. When they rode into the city from Delhi darwaza, fires lit up the sky to mark their progress. Akbari Mandi, then Hira Mandi, then . . . The soldiers looted, and torched what they could not loot. Before that fateful sun had set, the troops were baying for the blood of the Sandhawalias.

The Sardars prepared to fight. They laid out their garrison; they sent messengers out to the Khalsa troops. Come and talk to us, they said. Let us hold the Sikhs against the Dogras. But few of the chiefs came to the fort. And those who did failed to carry the men with them. Hira Singh had already promised them money and convinced them that the Sandhawalias were traitors.

At night campfires circled the fort. The siege was complete and the sound of cannonfire followed its own echo without a break. The shrieks that rose from the lanes hung in the night air and then fell and were lost in the tumult raised by the riders and the horses. The drums began to beat louder with every passing hour.

All night the guns roared. When the pink dawn lit up the far side of the Ravi and the first birds took to wing from the thorny kikar trees, thousands of men entered the fort through the breached walls and it was all over for the Sardars. Ajit Singh Sandhawalia attempted to escape by swinging down the wall of the fort on a rope near the Alamgiri bund. But the rope broke and as he lay injured some soldiers cut off his head. They carried the speared head to Hira Singh who in turn laid it at the feet of his stepmother, Rani Pathani. 'Now I can die a proud wife and mother,' she said. Dhian Singh's body was pieced together from the foundry pit and dressed for cremation. Rani Pathani climbed the pyre, and she took her poor slave girl into the fire with her.

Lehna Singh was found hiding in a vault, his thigh shattered by bullets. They cut up his body and hung it in the four corners of Lahore. When the bloodbath was over, it had been three days of terror and madness. A thousand men had been killed.

The Sandhawalias had already announced Duleep would be Maharaja. Hira Singh could do no better. The five-year-old Duleep was a convenient choice for him too. The other acknowledged sons of Ranjit Singh were much older.

And so Duleep was taken to the Shish Mahal. I was there when Hira Singh, his thin face flush with victory, stepped forward and knelt to kiss the child's feet. Our Dula ji was acknowledged as king from the Khyber to the Sutlej and word went out that Raja Hira Singh Dogra, son of Raja Dhian Singh, would be Wazir.

Duleep Singh, autumn 1893, Paris

There are fading memories that I try to cling on to. Sometimes I see them clearly, at other times I struggle to drag them back from some dark abyss. I see my horses and elephants, elephants always with red and gold howdahs, their wise eyes looking at me sideways. I see my troop of sixty young boys whom I used to drill as soldiers, giving them commands, leading them into battle. I see my tutors of Persian and Gurmukhi, I see my valets holding out dresses for me to choose every morning, I see the treasurer's son holding out a large tray of jewels for me to choose what to wear for the day.

And often I see huge tents, yellow and red striped canopies. The ground covered with carpets. Carpets with swirling designs and flowers and birds. A carpet with a large lion on its hind legs, poised to attack, a spear already through its heart. We were in a large garden, I remember, with short orange trees all around. Next to me was my maternal uncle, Jawahar Singh, and on my other side was the Wazir, Hira Singh. And behind me the man whom I used to be really frightened of, the man who used to threaten me every time he looked at me with his dark, cruel eyes. Pandit Jalla. I hated to be alone with Pandit Jalla. He was always there whenever anything important was to happen; he was like the shadow of Hira Singh.

But the memory of that day, with its fresh cool breeze and its lambent sunlight is only a pleasant memory.

I sat in a chair and many important people came forward, bent towards me and gave me presents. I used to talk about that memory many times and finally, nearly twenty years later, my mother told me that I could only be thinking of the Dussehra festival, in October 1843, less than a month after I had ascended the throne. I realize now why I was there; I was a convenient puppet. Hira Singh and Pandit Jalla were there because they were the actual rulers of Punjab. Jawahar Singh was there since he was my uncle. And the tents that I remember were very famous tents—they could be put up without poles, the same tents that had been used more than ten years earlier by my father when he set up camp for receiving the then Governor General William Bentinck at Ropar, on the Sutlej.

Some things one does not forget, no matter how much time passes.

Mangla, winter 1893, Hardwar

Who cares for a five-year-old, even if he is a Maharaja? That was the way it was. Duleep was a child in the durbar, while the real business of the court carried on around him. And what dirty business it was. Every type of haramgiri was practised there. Lavish entertainments, intrigues, conspiracies. Now when I look back, even I feel guilty for being part of it all. But I was under the influence of Jawahar Singh and he was always looking for pleasure. Earlier I had known him only as the younger brother of Rani Jindan, one who wouldn't walk by without a smile that always pulled at my heartstrings. He used to be a careless boy, roaming the bazaars of Lahore, busy flying his hawk in the day, intoxicated in the evenings.

But ever since he had been put in charge of Duleep, his walk had changed. He dressed as a Sardar of the durbar and when he came to talk to his sister, I felt proud that I knew him well. But one thing had not changed. He would still always look towards me and his look would linger and then he would smile the same heartbreaking smile. And not once did he ask me to leave the room, no matter what he had to discuss with Jindan. Often, he would wink at me as he passed; he would ask me to arrange the best dancing girls for his evening entertainment. I wasn't a fool—no, I knew these to be crumbs. But small people are easily pleased with the throwaway words and gestures of big people. Life would be unbearable otherwise. You understand this, don't you, Arur . . .

One day Jawahar Singh walked into Jindan's room in anger.

'He is your son,' he said, 'son of a king and not some pup. And yet, see what is happening all around. That haramzada Jalla controls everything; Hira Singh is a toy in his hands. Jalla gets a report on who comes and goes into the palace, what happens in which platoon. I hear now he is looking into each jagir granted by the Sarkar. If things go on like this, we will soon become dispensable.'

'I want to hang that Jalla from the peepal in front of Moti Mandir!' Jindan's eyes blazed in anger.

'Then do something, sister.'

'We will find a way; leave it to me. Suchet Singh is also fed up with them. He is our ally.'

'Raja ji,' she told Suchet Singh the very next day, 'I fear for Duleep. I cannot sleep with worry. He is but an innocent child. His future should be in my hands. Instead that Pandit has taken over the kingdom. Hira Singh does not lift a finger without looking to him.'

'Nobody knows that better than me,' Suchet Singh replied. 'Hira Singh is of my blood, the son of my brother. But I am not blind to his faults. He lives too much in Jalla's sway. After all the support that

I gave him to finish off the Sandhawalias, he offers me nothing more than the governorship of Peshawar!'

'And I am stuck in the zenana,' Jindan continued. 'I should be ruling Lahore in place of my son till he grows up. Even the British have a Malka on the throne, why am I in the zenana? Am I less than any man? They take decisions about my son. I hear that Hira Singh has rejected a proposal of marriage sent for Duleep by the Sardar sahib of Ropar and I wasn't even consulted.'

She tried her best, egged on by Jawahar Singh and of course by me. But Suchet Singh could not get past his elder brother, the old fox Gulab Singh, who told him not to indulge in intrigues against his own flesh and blood. Suchet Singh went away to Jammu, but the fire that was running in his veins would erupt soon enough.

It rarely ever hails in the month of Magh; if fact it rarely even rains. In Magh the winter is departing and the earth is preparing to bring out fresh leaves and flowers. But on the day that the raj tilak was to be put on Duleep's forehead, the day chosen by the court astrologers, after looking at all the stars and their alignments, on that day it hailed like I have never seen it hail ever before, or since. There had not been a cloud in the sky when Duleep bathed and dressed up in his new garments. After bowing before the Granth Sahib he sat on the royal chair in the Shish Mahal. One by one, the priests dipped their thumbs in the silver bowl and fixed the tilak of saffron and white rice on his blessed young forehead.

My heart burst with pride as I watched. Here was the child whom I had brought up, whom I had fed and dressed, whom I had taught to walk, and he was finally sitting on the throne of Punjab, tilak on his forehead, kalgi in his turban. After that the Sardars, the army jarnails, the courtiers came before him one by one, presenting nazar, each according to his rank.

The guns sounded from the ramparts, wisps of smoke rose in the blue sky and the dancing began. In the courtyard outside the Shish Mahal, around the high fountains, the girls danced before the boy king. Everywhere there was joy—among the crowd in the fort, in the bustling bazaar, in the speeding winds.

Then like arrows from an attacking enemy, the hailstones fell.

Large hailstones, each one the size of a walnut, falling with the speed of avenging fate. The crowd dispersed fast, taking shelter in the halls and the corridors, under the eaves and in the verandas while the stones bounced off the marble, several feet into the air, making a noise that was like the din of battle. The sun vanished from the darkened sky and night fell early. A hush fell over the durbar.

The whispers began: something had gone wrong; more terrible days would follow. The kingdom was cursed; the rule of Hira Singh and Pandit Jalla had not been blessed by the gods. And pity the young child put on the throne . . .

There was no letting up in the omens. In a few days, once again an auspicious time turned dark and hail fell. It was the Sankrant of Chet, a day for good deeds and clean living. On a similar Sankrant day the Sandhawalias had done the unthinkable and killed Sher Singh. Hailstones fell all over the kingdom, killing the crops where they stood, a month before the harvest.

It was clear to anybody who cared to see: Evil days had been foretold and evil days were upon us. When the blood of innocents is spilt, when brother kills brother, when salt is betrayed, only evil can happen.

How else do I explain the locusts that came from the south, thousands, lakhs, crores of locusts, whirling forth like messengers of death? Scarcely did one wave pass than another was seen over the river, preparing its assault on the city. But it was not the city that was their target. They flew over us like a witch's curse, then over the fort, the gardens, the baradaris and khwabgahs, over the minarets of the Badshahi Masjid and to the fields beyond, which were already maimed by the hailstones. They descended on the yellowing wheat and corn with a ferocious hunger.

The farmers cursed them and cursed everything—the stars, the moon, the day, the year, the kings and the wazirs, the pandits and the chiefs. They even cursed Duleep, the young child who did not know the meaning of their curses, who cowered in fright as he saw the waves of insects flying over Summan Burj, eclipsing the sun. He kept waving them off, even when he slept fitfully at night.

The killing and the deception resumed. One day Jawahar Singh tried to seek the help of the Khalsa army against Hira Singh and

Jalla. He put Duleep on his elephant and rode towards the troops, hoping to appeal to them in the name of the young Maharaja.

'Help me, Khalsa ji,' he said, 'help me against the Dogra Hira Singh or let me go on to Ferozepur and get the help of the English.'

But the Khalsa soldiers did not help him. They had never approved of Jawahar Singh's licentious ways. They respectfully took away Duleep but put Jawahar under guard. The next day Hira Singh rode out to the troops, rewarded them handsomely and brought the Maharaja back to Summan Burj, ordering that the cannon be fired again from the ramparts. Jawahar Singh was dragged back in chains and thrown into prison. That night my heart pained for him. I buried my head in Jindan's lap and cried. She allowed me the gift of her silence, though she understood.

Hailstorms in the month of Magh or locusts eating the fields of wheat or the curse from a pyre or the prediction of a mad ghorcharha—the truth is that when dark days come, they cannot be held back. Much more blood was to flow in Lahore, many others would die. Duleep was on the throne, that is true, and Hira Singh was his Wazir. But the domination of the arrogant Jalla angered everyone— Rani Jindan, the Sardars at the court and most of all the Khalsa army. Many a soldier would have gladly forgiven Hira Singh much else if he had put a spear through the Pandit's heart.

The blood finally went to Suchet Singh's head. He rushed down towards Lahore with forty soldiers to challenge his nephew. A bloody battle was fought on the outskirts of the city. Suchet fought bravely, I heard, like a true Rajput, and died with a sword in his hand. Hira Singh cried like a child when he saw his uncle's dead body and cremated him with all respect and honours.

But not all the Khalsa troops had been bought over by Hira Singh. Many had gathered under the flag of the surviving Sandhawalia, Attar Singh, to do battle with Hira Singh and ensure that a Sikh became the Wazir of Duleep Singh. These things seemed to matter to those soldiers, and they were prepared to trade the honour of their kingdom for it. They struck a deal with the firanghis, who were only too happy to extend secret support.

The news spread like fire through the bazaars of Lahore and up to the fort; the memory of the havoc caused by the Sandhawalias was still fresh.

Hira Singh rushed out to the Khalsa army panchayats gathered under their fluttering flags beyond the ramparts of the fort.

'Another Sandhawalia snake,' he said, 'has been nurtured by the British. Have we forgotten what Lehna Singh and Ajit Singh did on these very ramparts, and that too at the behest of the wily British? And now Attar Singh Sandhawalia! Come with me, and let us squash this menace before it raises its head any further.'

He managed to convince the Panches. Khalsa soldier fought against Khalsa soldier on the banks of the Sutlej. Sandhawalia was killed and so was a holy man, Bhai Bir Singh. The army came back not only to the sound of gun salutes but also the taunts of their fellows: Gurumars! Killers of a Guru! Cholera broke out in the cantonment. It was the Bhai's curse, they said.

Then there was news of the coming of that Hardinge as Governor General. The Angrez saw our wretched future better than we did. They had begun to prepare for the coming battles.

But in Lahore, they were still fighting amongst themselves. I don't blame the firanghis—they owed us nothing. We destroyed ourselves.

It was a very cold day up in the fort, the Sankrant of the month of Poh. A damp mist hung outside the haveli window. Below us the poor and the needy had already begun to gather, shivering in their blankets, waiting patiently on the damp grass. They knew that Jindan would come out soon, with her generous charities. In a silver tray I had counted and put the pieces of gold and silver that we had demanded from the treasury the previous day. Carefully I covered it all with a red silk cloth.

'Everything is ready, Rani ji,' I stepped forward.

She nodded but just then, one of the slave girls came into the chamber.

'Maharani ji, the Pandit wants to see you.'

'Jalla?'

'Yes Maharani ji. He is outside, with some men.'

I accompanied Jindan to the balcony. Pandit Jalla stood below the haveli. He was an ugly man, with his huge moustache, his oily skin and cunning eyes. He was staring up at the balcony. Without any ceremony, he began shouting from where he stood.

'I hear you are planning great charities today, Mai ji.'

'Today is Sankrant and it is usual to give charity to the poor and the needy.'

'But not in the way you have decided to. I have seen what you have withdrawn from the treasury. You cannot give away the wealth of the Lahore durbar like this.'

'I will do what I want. Who are you to say this to me?'

'It seems I will have to show you who I truly am. Just because we have put your infant on the throne, it does not mean you rule over us. Your son graces the throne because of the brave sword of Dogra Hira Singh. Do not ever forget that.'

Jindan slammed the window shut and came into the chamber. Her face was afire with anger and her entire body quivered like a taut bowstring.

'The snake! How dare he talk to me like that! I will straighten him out.'

She paced up and down the chamber for a while, lost in thought. When she spoke again her voice was calm and her gaze steady. She looked every inch the beautiful, fiery queen that she was.

'I will speak to the Khalsa troops about this. The time has come to show Jalla who really rules Lahore,' she said. My Rani could be a tigress when challenged.

The Khalsa troops were already angry with Hira Singh because he had fired a few hundred troopers just days earlier. Rani Jindan's complaint against Jalla fell on dry grass and the fire that she lit raced through the cantonments. The troops could no longer be kept confined there. From the walls of the fort I could see the tents being pitched on the plains near the Ravi and I waited, with bated breath, for the storm to break.

A few days later, elephants loaded with boxes of jewels and coins were seen moving out of the fort early in the morning, heading towards Taxali darwaza. Hira Singh and the Pandit were leaving before the soldiers attacked. But they didn't get far. Sham Singh Attariwala and his men chased them down. Before that sun had set, the heads of Hira Singh and his jarnails were hanging from the branches outside Lohari darwaza. And as for Pandit Jalla, the Nihangs were riding through the bazaars with his head on a spear, covered with a saffron scarf. If someone gave them a few kauris, they would remove the scarf and let people see the head of the villain. It was a fearful evening and I stayed inside with Jindan and the young Maharaja. We did not want him to hear of such things.

Hira Singh and Jalla were dead and it seemed that the rule of the Dogras over Lahore durbar was finished, once and for all. There were celebrations when Jawahar Singh went to Hira Singh's house and brought away his treasure—at least thirty lakh worth—and showed it to us. It seemed that good times awaited us all. Mangla, I said to myself, thank your God because your life has changed forever.

But who was to predict the ways of the Khalsa soldiers? A group of them sought a meeting with Jindan.

'Mai ji,' their leader said boldly, 'I hear that you plan to make your brother the Wazir.'

'And what is wrong with that?'

'A son of a kennel keeper cannot be Wazir of Lahore.'

'And why not? I am the daughter of the same kennel keeper and my son is on the throne of Lahore.'

The soldiers were quiet for a while. Then one of them spoke again.

'Why not make Peshaura Singh the Wazir? He too is a son of the Sarkar. And you need a man like him. There is unrest everywhere.'

'So you have come to plead Peshaura Singh's case,' said Jindan sharply. 'How much has he paid you? Here, go tell the troops that Mai Jindan has raised every man's salary by half a rupee and let me not hear Peshaura's name again in this durbar.'

'Long live Mai Jindan!' the soldiers shouted. 'Long live Duleep Singh!'

But at night, Jindan dictated a letter to Peshaura Singh. Stay away from Lahore and I promise you a jagir, was her straightforward message to him. Peshaura Singh stayed away and finally, on the eighth day of the month of Jeth, my favourite Jawahar was made Wazir and I saw him receiving nazar from big and small, his whole

body covered with ornaments. My mistress had become a real
woman, a scheming, intelligent, beautiful queen.

Those were some of the happiest days of my life, Arur. My Duleep
was on the throne. And Jawahar didn't forget me when he became
Wazir. Many a tamasha did I organize for him in his haveli, with
dancing girls, wine, music and afeem . . . In the haveli of my Jindan,
those were the days of Lal Singh. He had become the favourite of my
mistress. He was a clever man, that Brahmin who had used the
Dogras well. Dhian Singh made him head of the toshakhana. Then
Hira Singh made him a Raja, putting the tilak on his forehead with
his own hand. But Lal Singh knew that the future was with Jindan
and Duleep. The day Hira Singh was killed, he was the first to come
and give Jindan the news. She had a weakness for him, for soon she
was showering him with all her favours. She was still young, after all,
and now the most powerful woman in Punjab—why, in those
months no man had greater power. None of this was going too well
with the Khalsa soldiers. They thought that they were the pure ones,
the keepers of the Sikh faith. They didn't like Jawahar's ways and
they did not like Jindan's closeness to a man who was not even a
Sikh . . .
       There I go again, an old woman jabbering away, moving from
one story to another. But that is the way my mind is nowadays. I
must tell you whatever comes to my mind, or I may forget it all
forever.

Bamba, Bamba . . . that was the name of Duleep's queen finally. I
have heard she too has passed on some years ago. She bore him his
children and may God give them a long life . . . but she was not one
of our own. And then I heard the name of this Englishwoman from
you, Arur—Ada, or something like that? What sort of a name is that,
I ask you? I have heard names of Englishwomen before, but I have
never heard such a name. We could never have thought that he
would marry such women. Rani Jindan had chosen a bride for him
when he was eight. Tej Kaur, daughter of Chatar Singh Attariwala.
How we celebrated the betrothal! It was in the month of Har of the
English year 1845. The lamps did not go out in Summan Burj all

night and music drifted over the fort till dawn. The shagun came in the month of Sawan when dark clouds had massed in the sky and the peacocks danced near the river.

But marriages they say are made in heaven and that marriage was not to be. The British did not let it happen and the girl's father and brother, Chatar Singh and Sher Singh, fought them at Chilianwala . . . But of all that, some other time.

Those days, I used to go regularly to pray to Lord Shiva at the temple that Jindan had built specially for me just near Masti darwaza. She had a large and generous heart, my Maharani, and she knew how to reward those who served her. Nobody took care of that temple after our lives changed yet again and Jindan, Duleep and I were banished to different places. It has been so long, our exile, and only death can put an end to it . . . I finally returned to that temple a few years ago and got it repaired. New bells, new doors, new idols. I had to do it for Jindan's memory—and for Duleep's. It still belongs to him; they didn't take it away, like they did his fort and palace and toshakhana.

So much still belongs to him. The villages, havelis, gardens in Gujranwala, Jhelum, Gurdaspur, Lahore, Amritsar, Pothohar . . . If they had given him even one of those havelis, even a handful of those villages, it would have been better than any place that he was given to stay in Vilayat. He would not have had to beg them for money less than some shopkeepers make in Vilayat, from what you tell me. That country of white men should be ashamed of itself . . .

So I was saying, I would go to the Shiva temple every day. Things began to go wrong on one such day just after I had performed my prayers there and handed over many bags of flour in charity. I was walking back to the fort when I ran into a large crowd.

'They are burying the Immortal Fakir!' one of my girls told me.

That was another miracle of those years—the Immortal Fakir. He used to be tied up in a sack and sealed—even in Ranjit Singh's time, with the Maharaja's own seals—and then he would be suspended deep in a vault under the earth and everything would be covered up as if it had not been dug up at all. The place was guarded day and night by sentries. Months later, the Fakir would be dug out. Slowly his body would become alive again, his eyes would open, his tongue would straighten out. He would begin to speak even as the astounded Maharaja and his firanghi guests watched. The fakir did this many times, staying without food, water, air for months.

And now they were doing it again. I stopped for a minute to look and I still remember his frightening, cruel face, with sharp eyes and a hooked nose. His body was smeared with ash and two men were tying up his feet and hands.

'Let's go,' I ordered the girls. 'I don't like him. I hope they bury him so deep that he cannot come out.'

But we didn't go very far. At the next chowk, Shah Mohammed was standing under the old banyan tree. He often used to come there when he had a story to tell. A crowd had gathered to listen to him—shopkeepers, mahouts, ghorcharhas, Nihangs.

A brave soldier, a true son of Ranjit, Peshaura Singh was master of Attock fort. Only last summer he took the fort with just seven men and now he commanded two thousand warriors, with their guns, with their horses. He sent parwanas to the villages around Attock—I am King of Lahore, son of Ranjit.

How would that be liked here, my people, how would that be taken by your Jawahar Singh?

So the plan was hatched right here, in Summan Burj. Jawahar, brave with wine, sent his hired assassins. They rode day and night, and when Peshaura hunted boar at Hasan Abdal, there where Baba Nanak stopped a boulder with his palm, they caught up with him. Back to Attock they took the brave Khalsa, back to the dungeons of the fort. And there while he challenged them to fight like men, they cut him to pieces and flung him into the Indus.

The poet sees only trouble ahead, only trouble . . .

A young warrior jumped up next to the poet. His naked sword glinted in the sun. His eyes were red with rage.

'That luchcha kanjar Jawahar Singh! How dare he kill a son of Ranjit Singh? All night he is drunk, lying with his kanjaris. This sword will now be sheathed only when it has drunk Jawahar's blood. His sister must give him up.'

Another, wearing the tall blue turban of the Nihangs, joined him, the pike in his hand tearing at the sky.

'Rani Jindan will have to give up her cowardly brother. Or she and her infant will be treated as traitors to the Khalsa Panth. This will be the command of the Sarbat Khalsa.'

A war cry rose from the crowd: 'Jo Bole so Nihal—'

The response from the crowd was so loud that it seemed to shake the walls of the fort:

'Sat Sri Akal!'

My blood ran cold. The anger of the faithful roused by zealots is a terrible thing. I hurried back to the fort. To my shock, I saw that the palace was being illuminated with rows and rows of little lamps. Jawahar, my foolish lover, was celebrating Peshaura's death, unaware of the fury that was building up among the soldiers.

We got the news of the return of Fakir Nuruddin early in the morning.

'Let him eat something and present himself,' Jindan ordered, even though I knew how anxiously she had been waiting for his return.

She had hardly slept since the time that the army had formally branded Jawahar Singh a traitor. He must be handed over, the court was told. The orders had been issued under the seal of the Khalsa and everybody understood what that meant. The army panchayats were representing the Sikh commonwealth and were committed to holding up the interests of the community. They could not be denied; they had the cover of faith. Immediately it had been decided by Jindan and Jawahar to send three wise men of the court—the Fakir, Dewan Deena Nath and Attar Singh Kalianwalla—to negotiate with the army chiefs and now it all depended upon what they had managed to do.

But I knew that there was little hope as soon as Fakir ji entered the haveli, his eyes downcast. He bowed low before Jindan and Jawahar and with folded hands and quivering voice he told us what we least wanted to hear.

'Mai ji, we have failed you. In fact, the others have not even been allowed to come back to the fort by the soldiers; only this unfortunate being has been sent to convey their evil intentions to you.'

Jindan tried to keep her voice under control.

'What do they say, Fakir ji? Are they bent on their evil designs or is there any hope of compromise?'

'I am afraid not, Mai ji. Their anger is flowing over. The poison has been spread deep and wide by Raja Gulab Singh. His men, led by his son, have been handing over bags of coins to soldiers and spreading evil gossip about Jawahar Singh ji. In fact, even as we speak, I know that four battalions of infantry have started from Mian Mir for Lahore. If by tomorrow Jawahar Singh ji is not handed over to them, they have vowed vengeance against the entire fort.'

Then, glancing at Jawahar Singh, who stood frozen with fear, the Fakir added in a low tone: 'The killing of Peshaura Singh and the celebrations in the fort have wounded the soldiers deeply.'

'I do not grieve for Peshaura Singh,' said Jindan. 'His existence was a constant threat to Duleep.'

But even as she spoke, all of us realized what the Fakir meant.

'What do we have to do then, Fakir ji, if they have not listened to you?'

'I am afraid there is little choice left, Mai ji.'

'What do you mean? Hand over my own brother to them to be killed?'

'The panchayats have commanded that Jawahar Singh ji must present himself to them within forty-eight hours and be tried by the army tribunal.'

'Or else?'

'They will roll up the artillery to the fort and blast open the gates and put all the residents of the fort to the sword. They will show no mercy, Mai ji, they have blood on their minds.'

Jawahar Singh exploded.

'Have you all lost your senses? I am the Rani's brother, uncle of the Maharaja, the Wazir of the durbar. How can you hand me over? You have to protect me with all your strength.'

He stared in mounting panic at his sister and then at the Fakir and then back at his sister.

There was a steely edge in her voice when she spoke.

'These troops have gone mad. Power has gone to their heads. Veer ji, I will try everything that I can but both you and I know that there is little choice but for us now to go to them. We do not have the strength to deny the decision of the Sarbat Khalsa. I will go to them with Duleep and say that here too is a son of Ranjit Singh. For his sake, I will ask them to spare you.'

Jawahar Singh did not give up easily. That night he offered half a lakh rupees to the two battalions in the fort to help him escape. But the troops had received their orders from the army panchayats too; they did not want to incur the wrath of their fellows. They refused to open the gates of the fort. And the next morning, beyond the ramparts, across the broad plain that led to the cantonment at Mian Mir, I saw a long line of men in perfect formation, marching towards the fort. The Khalsa army was already on the move . . .

But before I bring up the story of the day when he finally came face to face with his God, let me say what I have to say about Jawahar Singh. To me he was always kind. And that much was enough. For that kindness I served him well, provided for his pleasure and excess. I did enough to be ashamed of and I felt no shame. I considered myself fortunate that I, a slave girl first sold by her own father, should now be the lover of the Wazir of Lahore. This is destiny. And who would have imagined that I would end up even as the controller of that house of riches, the toshakhana. The mirasi who bought and sold me so often, so many years ago, for a few kauris would, if he were to have seen me, cut his own throat.

Or I would have killed him, with my bare hands.

Duleep Singh, autumn 1893, Paris

There is a dream, curse it, which will not go away. It has haunted me for close to fifty years, and always when I am sad or sick. Its images do not change; its colours do not fade. It will go away only when I die. That should not be too long now. Already my vision fades, my words slur on to each other, my voice trails away. Ada, her mother, even Victor, when they are sitting in that chair—they sometimes look away even while I am trying to talk, as if I am already gone, already one with the past. I suppose they will all be relieved when I am gone. In many ways I must be an embarrassment, a burden.

But the dream . . . the bright sunshine of Mian Mir. It seemed so far away from Lahore fort then. I am on an elephant, sometimes I am alone and sometimes there is my uncle holding me by the shoulders. The elephant heaves and lurches down the slope, I hold on to the silver edge of the howdah. I can see the mahout's thick neck. He turns and looks up from time to time. He is a man with no teeth, red eyes and big gold earrings. And then there are screams and shouts. I hear a scream from my uncle, from the pit of his stomach, a scream that goes through me. Spears appear suddenly above the edge of the howdah and the sun reflecting off them knifes my eyes. I see below me faces distorted in anger, and turbans—blue, bright yellow. From somewhere far away I hear the voice of my mother above the din, pleading, wailing, a long wail that seems to rise above the walls of the fort behind us and hang in the sky and then fall, like a burnt-out star.

And then I am being pulled off the elephant by several strong hands and there are red fountains that are shooting up, fountains of blood from my uncle's chest, then his neck . . . towards a bright blue sky—and then there is a final shriek . . . and I wake up. These last few days, I see the dream almost every night and I wake up shivering, holding my own throat.

Mangla, winter 1893, Hardwar

Panic spread quickly in the bazaar with the approach of the army battalions. The shopkeepers pulled down their shutters before the sun had reached its height and ran homewards, carrying their valuables with them. When the sound of the approaching drums and bugles was heard in the fort Jawahar Singh broke down in front of Jindan. His body shook with fear.

'Nothing seems to work, I have offered the Panches an increase of twelve rupees a month and they have refused,' he said.

Jindan acted swiftly. She ordered that two elephants be loaded with silver. She still hoped to buy over the troops. The other members of the durbar also joined the procession and soon a long line of durbar elephants began to move out from the palace down the slope towards the gate of the fort.

A terrible fear clutched at my heart as we moved out under a clear blue sky. The bright afternoon sun reflected off the swords in the hands of the soldiers in the distance as they rode in formation towards us. Then the guns began to fire a salute, and it went on and on. Each cannonshot seemed to drive in the finality of the decision of the army: Jawahar Singh would not be spared. But still I prayed and still I hoped.

The soldiers slowed down to a trot as they reached us and quietly surrounded our procession and turned back towards the camp. We were already captives. Would we all be put to the sword? Or maybe the troops would spare us since they still respected Duleep, whom Jawahar had carefully put in his own howdah along with bags full of silver coins, gold and jewels.

I sat along with Rani Jindan on the second elephant. That day she looked every inch a queen, dressed in pure white, her face veiled.

Slowly our elephants moved into the camp and began to file past the silent battalions. All around there were the fierce faces of the soldiers, their eyes fixed on the first elephant with the young Maharaja and Jawahar in the howdah. Suddenly, the bugles broke the silence and the drums began to roll relentlessly.

A soldier on a white horse rode in front of the elephants and commanded loudly.

'Stop!'

Another soldier rode up to Jawahar's elephant and commanded it to kneel.

Rani Jindan spoke from where she sat. I could feel her body quivering.

'Khalsa ji, as commanded we are before you. My brother has sinned but has now come to seek forgiveness. And all our scriptures say that anyone who has come to seek mercy should be granted mercy. Khalsa ji, you have the power to forgive, to take in your embrace the sinner. I will be indebted to you till the end of time if you forgive my brother now. I will be obedient henceforth to the army. I will reward you handsomely.'

Silently, ten horsemen moved forward to our elephant from the formation and made our elephant kneel before them. One of them addressed Jindan.

'Mai, we have always respected you and shall continue to do so, but your brother is disloyal. He has tried to get the support of the British against us and he has acted on his own to kill Peshaura Singh. The Khalsa will show him how justice is done in Punjab. Now, get out of the way, Mai. Go to that tent.'

'I will not go anywhere,' she shouted. 'I will not leave my brother at your mercy.'

And then the nightmare began. Two soldiers stepped forward, took her by the arms and dragged her towards the tent, even while she shrieked, pleading for mercy for her brother.

One of the chiefs ordered Jawahar Singh: 'Let the Maharaja be taken care of. Hand him to us.'

'Take what you want,' replied Jawahar. 'I have here gold and jewels, enough to make you rich for life. Take these and I promise you more, I promise more for every one of you.'

'Enough! Hand over the Maharaja!'

A soldier moved towards the kneeling elephant and standing up in his stirrups slapped Jawahar Singh across the face. He then picked the child from his arms and pulled him out of the howdah. The Maharaja was taken into a tent and handed over to Rani Jindan. Immediately she held up the boy in her arms and cried: 'Spare my brother, for the sake of this child, this child of Ranjit Singh, this young Maharaja Duleep Singh.'

But the soldiers were not listening. One of them climbed the elephant and stabbed Jawahar Singh in the side. Another put a musket to the poor man's temple even as he fell and pulled the trigger. The devils did not stop even after that. They stabbed him and fired their muskets into him until his body was full of holes. Jindan's wails were louder than the gunshots. I don't remember if I cried out. Even in those moments of pain greater than any I will experience, I think I knew my place.

We were safe in the tent but we were under close guard. Duleep was taken away to another tent. All night Jindan wailed for her dead brother who lay on the ground only a few yards away, but the Sikh soldiers paid her no heed. They were celebrating the death of Jawahar Singh. They had avenged Peshaura Singh. They had done their duty for the Khalsa Panth.

At first light, Rani Jindan threw herself along with Duleep on her brother's dead body, wailing and pulling at her open hair. But what was there to do? Jawahar Singh lay dead on the ground, more than fifty holes in his body. She wanted to take him to cremate him in Badami Bagh but the soldiers would not allow that. Finally they relented and we took the body back to the Shish Mahal and waited for his widows and slave girls to get ready to perform sati. Jindan herself dressed two of the young widows, blessing them with new clothes and jewellery and bathing them for the last time. That same night, the widows and the slave girls climbed the pyre outside Masti darwaza and willingly became ash. There are many ways to kill, Arur. And many ways to make a virtue of brutality.

People used to beg for the blessings of the women who became sati—queens or slave girls. Their curses were greatly feared. What the Sikh soldiers did to the widows of Jawahar Singh even as they sat on the pyre was unthinkable. They snatched their jewels from their hands; they pulled off their necklaces, even pulled the earrings off their ears, the noserings off their noses. And all the time the soldiers laughed. The louder the widows cursed, the more raucous was the laughter that answered them.

I still remember the words of those women. They seemed so prophetic then, as if not the young widows but God was uttering them:

Punjab will be in chains. The Sikhs will be conquered by the sword. The country will be desolate and its skies will echo only the laments of widows. And yet, Rani Jindan will live long and happily and Maharaja Duleep Singh shall continue to reign.

A sati's words can also be wrong. Poor Rani Jindan did not live long, at least not in Punjab. Her days of glory began and faded in a very short time. And Maharaja Duleep, the unfortunate soul, now buried in a cold and distant land, and even when he reigned in Punjab it was only as a puppet . . .

Two days later, when the pyre had cooled, we went to collect the ashes of Jawahar and the satis and consigned them to the Ravi. Jindan's anger at the Khalsa army was unrelenting.

'You killed my innocent brother, at a time when he was not even wearing his armour. He came to you as a supplicant, not to fight you. You killed him like a butcher kills a lamb, listening neither to his entreaties nor to mine. I promised you obedience and loyalty and rewards but you would have none of it. Now there is only vengeance to be had. Your destruction is written and soon it shall come.'

Shah Mohammed sang of her grief and her anger in the bazaars of Lahore:

Those who killed my brother, I swear
Shall be dragged by their long hair.
Their cries shall be heard in foreign lands
Like goats slaughtered, these Khalsa bands,
And countless women without bangles on their hands.
O Shah Mohammed, widows' wails will rent the sky
When these Khalsa murderers die.

They say that there are two things that can cause havoc—a woman's tongue and an army in turmoil. Lahore was cursed with both. Day and night, Jindan thirsted for revenge.

'I will take them on as a man,' she told me soon after Jawahar Singh's funeral. 'They will see that I am not a woman whom they can push away. Tomorrow, I will take off this veil and challenge them openly.'

And that was what began to happen. Thousands of soldiers would enter the fort bristling and shouting, weapons in hand, and when she appeared without a veil, a hush would descend upon them. They would be quelled by the fire in those eyes, the passion that glistened on that forehead. Things came to such a pass that the brigades began to vie with each other to be in her durbar and promised to be faithful as long as they were allowed to see her unveiled when they wanted.

'Mai ji, the army panchayats would like nothing better than that you be the power in Punjab as long as the Maharaja is a child,' they said. 'Only turn Raja Lal Singh away from your palace. He is not one of us. Marry among the Sikh chiefs. Else how do we continue to call you the mother of all Sikhs?'

But there were circles within circles. The men around her resented the power of the army panchayats. They were keen to free themselves of their control and make quick personal gains. That is why they used to counsel her that war with the British would be a good way of keeping the army in its place.

'Finish them off, Rani ji,' they said. 'Pit the Khalsa soldiers against the British armies. They are already gathering across the Sutlej—men in red coats, horses, camels, even boats have been brought from Bombay. Make the Khalsa go to war. Throw this serpent in the lap of the enemy.'

So they continued to provoke the Khalsa army to cross the Sutlej. On a cold Katak evening in Shala Bagh, Dewan Deena Nath stood up in the hall with the marble pillars and spoke to army Panches and Sardars.

'Bad days are upon us,' said the Dewan. 'If we do not pull together our forces, the redcoats will swamp us. All the signs have been there for a long time, only we have been blind. Wake up, Khalsa ji, open your eyes before it is too late. Have they returned the treasures buried in their territory by Raja Suchet Singh? Have they given us back the village of Moran? Across the river, I get reports every day, they treat our Sikh brethren like slaves of the empire. Wake up, Khalsa ji, keep your determination and your strength. Keep alive in your hearts the memory of the noble Sarkar and victory will surely be yours. Do not vacillate any longer. Or it will be too late. But first you need a Wazir and you need a Commander-in-Chief. Maharani Jindan has proposed Raja Lal Singh to be your Wazir and Sardar Tej Singh to be your Commander-in-Chief. Khalsa ji, accept these appointments and prepare for war.'

I don't know how but the army agreed to appoint the two men they did not like. But now I can see it clearly, it was its darkest hour. I am old now and must only tell the truth. Ganga Mai is my witness, those two men would turn out to be our biggest traitors, traitors to Jindan, to the armies, to Punjab.

A few days later, a ceremony was held at the samadh of the noble Sarkar. One by one, the new Wazir, the new Commander-in-Chief, the army Panches and the Sardars put their hand on the Guru Granth and swore allegiance.

'We will fight, we will die for Maharaja Duleep Singh. May God give us strength.'

Arur Singh, winter 1905, Lahore fort

Living with our last Maharaja, I learnt of how we were betrayed, how
we, of the Punjab, betrayed ourselves, how we enabled British
soldiers to swagger around our palaces. Maharaja Duleep Singh read
every report and letter he could find, to understand how Punjab was
tricked. I learnt of it from him. I was familiar with some of what
Mangla Mai told me in Hardwar.

Ellenborough, the Governor General, had set his target: war
with the Sikhs was to be engineered by November 1845. In a letter
to Duke Wellington he wrote: 'Everything is going on there as we
could desire if we looked forward to the ultimate possession of the
Punjab . . .'

Yes, thanks to our own short-sightedness and greed, everything
was going his way. The durbar was fighting its own army, the
courtiers were plotting for their own survival, the army did not trust
the palace and was bent on establishing the absolute rule of the
Khalsa. Raja Gulab Singh, too, was in the game, quietly fomenting
trouble between the durbar and the army and promising connivance
to the British . . . Yes, everything was going the way the British
wanted it. The season of swords would not be long in coming. And
traitors would flourish.

Ellenborough's successor, Henry Hardinge, continued to
strengthen the British position. Men and weapons moved to the
cantonments at Ludhiana, Ferozepur, Ambala, Meerut, Kasauli,
Sabathu . . . Elephants, camels, horses, bullocks, even boats were
brought close to the Sutlej. These movements could have sent only
one signal to the Khalsa army, and that was the one that was
intended: the British were planning to invade Punjab. And Major
Broadfoot, the British Agent at Ludhiana, was a man who loved to
bait the Sikhs. He began to assiduously treat with the traitors and
provoke the army by behaving as if the durbar's territories that lay
on the east bank of the Sutlej were in British hands already. More
provocation was provided by the traitors.

One evening at the sacred samadh of Maharaja Ranjit Singh, Lal
Singh and Tej Singh addressed the Army Panches.

'Khalsa ji, the time has come to do battle. Guru Gobind gave you the sword not to let it rust. The redcoats gather like locusts around us; soon they will feed upon us mercilessly. They will do to us what they have done to Tipu and the Mahrattas. Are we going to let that happen? Is the Khalsa so scared for his own skin?'

The pride of the Sikh soldiers was challenged. Their eyes were set on the battlefield; their blood, against their better counsel, was astir. 'We desire peace,' said one of the generals, but his hand was on his sword. 'We are not foolish to march against the British on our own, but if their armies march to Ludhiana and Ferozepur, then by the blessings of Guru Gobind we too will march.'

Yes, unfortunately all was going according to plan. All that was needed was a cause to declare war. And when this would not come, it was manufactured. On the 6th of December 1845, the British armies began to move towards the frontier. The Khalsa army watched patiently. When British intentions were unmistakable, the first detachments of the Khalsa army crossed the Sutlej and were camped in their own territory to better watch the British movements. No treaty was breached; there was no act of aggression. Yet it was enough. On the 13th, Hardinge declared war on the Sikhs and annexed all the territories of Maharaja Duleep Singh that lay on the left bank of the Sutlej. The target set by Ellenborough had been missed only by a month.

Mangla, winter 1893, Hardwar

Then Shah Mohammed sang of the battles.

> *A village by the name of Mudki,*
> *The two armies face to face,*
> *The brave ghorcharhas, their flags held high—*
> *But the firanghi's guns blow them into the sky!*
> *O Shah Mohammed! The Khalsa is on the run,*
> *The guns abandoned, the battle is done.*

Mudki, Pherushahr, Sabraon . . . Lahore echoed with the sounds from these battlefields. Tales of Punjabi soldiers' bravery and the treachery of their own leaders became songs and legends within hours. The Khalsa army fought every inch; the redcoats had not imagined such opposition. But in the end, that cursed Lal Singh and that greater scoundrel Tej Singh misled the armies again and again, deserted them in mid-battle, leaked the battle plans to the British.

I waited loyally beside Rani Jindan in the palace and the news-bearers brought us reports every hour.

'A delegation of soldiers is on its way to you, Rani ji,' one of them said to us in the Shish Mahal, when the battle of Sabraon was building up.

'What do they want from me?' I noticed an edge in Jindan's voice as she spoke. We were not sure those days how the army would treat us.

'They have been betrayed by their own Wazir and Commander-in-Chief,' the news-bearer said. 'They have shed blood, fighting valiantly like Guru Gobind's Khalsa that they are. But they are now tired and angry, and they are hungry.'

When the delegation rode up to the fort, I saw just how angry and hungry they were. Gardona sahib told the Rani that she need not fear for her life, that she must meet them. He had placed four battalions of the infantry inside the fort to guard us in case the Sikh soldiers became unruly. Finally, convinced she was safe, she allowed the delegation to ride into the fort and come into the palace. Little Duleep was seated on the throne and I stood right next to the Rani behind the purdah that was always placed behind the throne.

'Maharani Jind Kaur,' the leader spoke in a loud voice, 'we have fought for you and we have fought for Maharaja Duleep Singh. May the Guru give him a long life. But we need your help.'

'What help can I give you?' Rani Jindan asked from behind the purdah. I looked at her face and once again I could only admire her. When she was alone, she was like any other woman would be—nervous, frightened, worried about her fate and the fate of her young son. But in a situation like this, a strange strength seemed to rise up from some deep well within her. Her face was composed, her eyes steady, her voice strong.

'We have been betrayed in the battlefield, betrayed by men who were your favourites—Lal Singh and Tej Singh. The scoundrels left us in mid-battle, they sold our secrets to the firanghi. They have robbed us of powder and they have deprived us of food. For three days our armies have fought on empty stomachs or filled them with raw grain and carrots.'

'Raja Gulab Singh has sent word that he has supplied food.'

'That old fox. And you trust him! The man who has sold his soul thirty-six hundred times! He meets us as a friend, he promises armies, he promises wheat, jagirs, kingdoms. But not one man rides up to join us, not one sack of wheat reaches us. He has not sent breakfast for a sparrow, forget about feeding an army. He is in league with the British.'

The voices from the other side of the purdah got louder and I feared for Duleep. The child just sat there, his eyes fixed on the angry soldiers in front of him, glued in fright to his throne.

Suddenly Jindan stepped back. In one motion she had slipped off her petticoat from under her dress, bunched it up and thrown it over the purdah into the midst of the startled soldiers.

'Here, you cowards!' she shouted, her face twisted in anger and contempt. 'Wear that and sit here, and eat your food and rest your limbs like women. I will wear trousers and ride into battle.'

There was a stunned silence and I feared the worst. I wanted to reach out for Duleep and pull him behind the purdah. But suddenly one of the soldiers shouted:

'Long live Duleep Singh Maharaja! We are going back to battle. We will fight for him and for the Khalsa Panth!'

They wheeled their horses and rode out of the fort. I collapsed in relief and tears flowed down my face as I watched Jindan step beyond the purdah and clasp Duleep to her heart.

Now, after all these years, I wonder whether what we did was for Duleep's good or not. Handing over the Khalsa army to men like Lal Singh and Tej Singh—was that not the beginning of the end for Duleep?

Duleep Singh, autumn 1893, Paris

I sometimes hear my mother challenge an army of Sikh soldiers—I don't hear the words, only a shout and an angry clink and clash of bangles, but I know it is a challenge. And then I feel the warmth of Bibiji's breath, her embrace. I think the memories are of the time when we lost our kingdom to Hardinge's men.

I was just a child; that is my only defence. The shame of it all!
The Sikhs provoked into war and then betrayed. The traitors living
right under my nose, in the comfort of our court. The clever
patience of the British.

Only when I sat in the libraries of London and went through the
papers of Ellenborough, Hardinge and Broadfoot did the whole
story become clear to me. I also chanced upon the memoirs of that
adventurer, Alexander Gardner, the one they used to call Gardona
sahib, whom I remember seeing often in the fort those days. 'Two
more contemptible poltroons than the two generals of the Khalsa
army, Lal Singh and Tej Singh, never breathed,' he wrote.

They outrage me, those words of the infamous proclamation of
war by Hardinge. To think that I have spent my life living among
such hypocrites, being more in tune with their ways and manners
and morals than with those of my father's. The phrases that the
English use make them sound like gods on earth. Everything to show
that they were always correct, always true, and the Sikhs always false.
They provoked and they goaded. They declared war when the Sikhs
were still in their own territory. And the treachery of the commanders
foisted on the Sikh army. I have read all that there is to read about
the first Anglo-Sikh war, of the battles of Mudki, Pherushahr,
Baddowal and Sabraon. I know how time and again Tej Singh and
Lal Singh did not press home the advantage gained by the Sikhs, how
they leaked the plans, how they vanished from the battlefield, leaving
the army leaderless. They were too keen to earn the goodwill of the
British, hoping for rewards after the war. Bibiji trusted these men
too long . . . until it was too late. And then when the armies would
no longer accept these traitors, she unfortunately brought back
Gulab Singh, who had already been in touch with the British,
promising allegiance in return for the protection of his possessions.
I cannot believe Bibiji acted out of anything but trust. She hadn't the
head of a ruler, she was only just learning to lead, and she made
mistakes—that is the worst anyone can say of her. The Sikhs would
be deceived and defeated and then they would be abandoned by
their own government. The British could cross the Sutlej unopposed;
the road to Lahore would be left open. And so it was.

Sometimes, when I read all this, I am not surprised that we lost
our kingdom. No kingdom could have survived such treason.

In my youth, in England, I have been to Hardinge's estate in Kent and ridden my charger along his hedges. He watched me with interest. I wonder what went on in his mind. He had once said that I was only 'a prince in fetters' who must do his bidding. He was the one who put me in those fetters.

I was too young then, but I remember, and now I understand. Henry Hardinge first humiliated me, the eight-year-old Maharaja of Punjab, by insisting I appear in person with my entire durbar at the Governor General's camp at Luliani where the terms of peace were finalized. Then I was led back to Lahore fort by British cavalry regiments and allowed to be escorted to the palace by my own courtiers. The aim, clearly, was to convey the impression that the Governor General was restoring to the young Maharaja his kingdom.

But soon, through the treaties of March 1846, the kingdom was parcelled out. The British took the fertile area between the Sutlej and the Beas. Jammu and Kashmir was handed over to Dogra Gulab Singh along with his brother Suchet Singh's hidden treasures. Lal Singh was retained as Wazir, Tej Singh as Commander-in-Chief. A garrison of British troops was moved into Lahore to stay till the end of the year while the Khalsa army was ordered to move across the Ravi. No Sikh soldier could enter Lahore without a permit. The one-armed Hardinge, whom the people of Punjab called Tunda Laat, had what he wanted: a weakened, pliant Punjab.

And I, the boy king, was left watching the scarlet flamingos dip into the fountains of the Shish Mahal while the British officers fondled the Koh-i-noor in amazement.

Mangla, winter 1893, Hardwar

After the Angrez had humbled us, with force and trickery, after they had broken up our Punjab, life was not the same. Not for me, not for Lahore. I did not feel powerful any longer. I was not even sure I had the influence any more to fix an audience, award a jagir, cancel someone's title ... This kanjari had that once. Briefly.

The Gora paltan was in the fort. The defeated Khalsa soldiers were locked up in Shahdara, their salaries reduced. Once in a while a band of ghorcharhas would venture towards Lahore but mostly they stayed away, roaming the villages. Their drums were silent; what did it matter that their blood was still hot.

The bolt of the firanghi's anger also finally fell on Lal Singh, that fox, though he had helped them so much in the battles! They decided that he had to be punished for delay in handing over Kashmir to Gulab Singh as had been decided in the treaties.

I, of course, knew the truth. Jindan's and Raja Lal Singh's conversations were private, but they were not private from me. The Rani never, till the end, thought that Lal Singh was capable of treachery. Perhaps she had her own reasons to trust him—she was not a fool, my firework of a Rani, she must have had a plan and perhaps Lal Singh was part of it. Perhaps. But she never told me.

'Gulab Singh has negotiated with the British that he will become ruler of Kashmir. That is why he deceived us during the battles. I will not let him have it,' Jindan had told Lal Singh.

'I will not leave a stone unturned to prevent it. I will tempt his enemy, Sheikh Imamuddin, to wage war against him,' Lal Singh assured her.

But the revolt was quickly quelled and Gulab Singh became ruler of Jammu and Kashmir. Lal Singh was hauled up in front of the British laats and removed from the palace under guard, no longer the Wazir. They picked up four pliable men to run the government—Dewan Deena Nath, Fakir Nuruddin, Sher Singh Attariwala and their favourite Tej Singh. This was their way of reducing further the power of my Jindan.

'We are all at your disposal, Mai ji,' Deena Nath came and told her. 'Sher Singh Attariwala will guard the palace. We know that we owe our lives only to you and to Maharaja Duleep Singh.'

I could see the anger building up in Rani Jindan's beautiful eyes. Anger with the British, with the courtiers, with the gods. She dismissed the men without a word and went back to her room, signalling to me to follow her.

'Lal Singh has gone because he was close to me,' she said, in a voice quivering with anger and frustration. 'I am the real target of the British; the real thorn in the flesh of the Tunda Laat. He knows that until he finishes me, Punjab will not be his.'

That day too would not be long in coming. The firanghi started his next game—of staying on in Lahore and getting rid of my mistress once and for all.

'How will they stay, Rani ji?' I asked her one day. 'They are to leave at the end of the year according to the treaties they have signed with us.'

'You will see, Mangla. They are here to stay, now that *we* have invited them in. Only, this time we will beg them to stay and they will, once they have me out of the way. But until then I will not give up.'

That Hardinge was a clever man. He knew that the Sardars around us were all up for sale, that all they wanted was to hold on to their jagirs. So he played on their fears. He spread the rumour that the British garrison would withdraw and there would be anarchy and chaos. He made them feel that they needed the permanent presence of the British in Lahore to protect them from each other.

In the end it was only Jindan who was still fighting to keep the Angrez out of Punjab. I remember how she addressed all the Sardars in the durbar in the month of Chet.

'I ask you one more time, all who are present. Do not make an Angrez the successor of Maharaja Ranjit Singh. Let me head the government with Duleep Singh on the throne. If anarchy is what you fear, then let the British give me two regiments, one of infantry and one of cavalry, with a battery of artillery and I shall ensure order.'

But the firanghi poison had already gone home. Most of the Sardars wanted to show their loyalty not to Jindan but to the Angrez. That way lay reward.

One by one they rose against her.

'This is not acceptable to us; this will never be acceptable to the British.'

'There will be chaos; already the British troops are moving in all directions.'

'If you want to destroy yourself and your son, Mai ji, go ahead, do as you please. You have only brought disgrace to this palace. We would rather align with the British.'

My mistress was left alone; the Tunda Laat had won the day.

Arur Singh, winter 1905, Lahore fort

There are papers that I personally unearthed for Duleep Singh in
London. They record how, outwitted by the British, tempted by
promises of reward, unnerved by fake troop movements, the ministers
and principal Sardars of Maharaja Duleep Singh's court gathered to
request the British troops to stay on in Punjab. The Treaty of
Bhyrowal was signed and ratified. Its terms were non-negotiable and
were not even seen by the Queen Mother Maharani Jindan, said to
be the mother of all Sikhs. A powerful British Resident—Henry
Lawrence to begin with—would be stationed in Lahore along with a
military garrison. The durbar would pay an annual amount of
twenty-two lakh new Nanakshahi rupees for its maintenance. A
Regency Council of eight was nominated to run the government.
Maharani Jindan was to be pensioned off with a lakh and fifty
thousand rupees; the courtiers agreed without much demur that she
need no longer have a role in running the state. Eight-year-old
Duleep Singh had already become a ward of the British government.
Hardinge, regretting that it had not been his fate to 'plant a British
standard on the banks of the Indus', could at least be satisfied that
he had performed the half-annexation.

Mangla, winter 1893, Hardwar

After Bhyrowal, our days of ruling the durbar seemed like a dream
of the past. Rani Jindan and I were, it seemed, destined to spend the
rest of our days in the zenana.

But she was not one to give up so easily. She was not made for
the zenana, for obedience and service. Only the lionheart had been
able to tame her.

'Mangla, I am as angry at the British as I am at my own people,'
she said to me. 'These Sardars, men whom the court of Ranjit Singh
has given every respect, these men who appear so proud and powerful,
are behaving like paid attendants of Lawrence—all for their jagirs,
for even bigger jagirs, titles, medals.'

'Rani ji,' I told her, 'this is the way of life. You are the Maharani,
the royal mother of the Maharaja, but even you know that today, the
British rule Lahore.'

'Rule Lahore indeed! Lying foxes! I will resist Lawrence to the end. Pray that the Guru gives me the strength to protect my son and what is rightfully his.'

Talking like this, she would walk up and down in her chamber all night, watching the sky light up and the night pass into day. I would lie down to sleep only when she did. I did not leave her for an instant those days. Her thoughts were my thoughts, her pain my pain . . .

Those were difficult days; there was chaos everywhere. Hundreds of disbanded Sikh soldiers roamed the countryside, humiliated and angry. A spark could set off anything those days. Like the time that the British sentries beat up some cows, these innocent holy animals. The people were angry, they threw stones from terraces. But Lawrence showed his iron fist. He caught one Brahmin from Lange Mandi and hanged him right there, in the middle of the bazaar. There had not been a hanging in Lahore for fifty years.

In those days of defeat, the soldiers and the common people began to see Jindan as the one who had been truly wronged, the one who had gained nothing in the end. Alone, she rose above all who had sold their souls. That is why the British feared her. They sought to lay every conspiracy at her door, so eager were they to besmirch her name and remove her from Lahore. When Prema, that old angry retainer of Gulab Singh, having lost his jagir hatched a plan to kill Lawrence, the blame fell on my mistress. But they could not pin anything on her. Nor could they do so when she sent Jawai—another girl whom she trusted a lot, though of course not as much as me—to meet Mulraj, the Governor of Multan. We sent her under the pretext of getting some white *ak* plants which grew in Multan and which we needed to perform a havan, but the real reason was of course to check if Mulraj was ready to rise against the British.

A year later he did, but by then the British had put my mistress where they wanted. Far away from Lahore. And they had thrown me out too. Me, just a slave girl, fortunate enough to be trusted, but they did not spare me.

That was when Lawrence decided to honour some loyal courtiers including Tej Singh.

'Tej Singh will become Raja of Sialkot? Not by the hand of my son!' Jindan was as angry as I had ever seen her. She stared out of the window into the dark night. 'The man who has conspired against me with the firanghi, the man who had Lal Singh deposed? Now he wants to be rewarded by the British for being their faithful dog. Let me see how they do that!'

Immediately we went to the Maharaja's chambers. She hugged Duleep tightly and said: 'Sit down, my son, and listen to me carefully. Difficult days are upon us. The British sahib is up to his tricks. He wants to reward your enemies tomorrow. They want to make Tej Singh a Raja by your hand. Do not, my son, put the tikka on his forehead when he bends before you. That is all you have to do, refuse to put the tikka. They can do nothing to you. You are the Maharaja. And I shall be standing behind you.'

The next day was one I can never forget. How can I? At the end of that day I was separated from my Jindan and Duleep. I was thrown into prison.

One of the girls brought in the message.

'The Maharaja is awaited in the takhtgah, Rani ji. The courtiers have come to escort him. The sahib is waiting too. The hour that the astrologers fixed is at hand.'

'The Maharaja is not yet ready,' Jindan replied brusquely. 'He will come as soon as he is.'

Only when a full hour had passed after the auspicious hour chosen by the astrologers did Jindan let Duleep move to the takhtgah. I moved behind the purdah along with her and watched the courtiers lead Duleep to the throne. I was scared for Duleep, and for all of us. The throne room was formally decorated for the occasion. The Englishmen were all in their shining red coats and black trousers; the Sardars were as usual vying with each other to show off their finery and their friendship with the British. I wondered what Duleep would do. The poor child was only nine.

We didn't have to wait long. The ceremonial announcements over, I saw Tej Singh step forward towards the throne with folded hands and bend down on one knee before Duleep. The silver bowl with the kesar and rice was extended towards Duleep and the entire court waited for him to anoint Tej Singh as the Raja of Sialkot.

But Duleep was his mother's true son. He stood perfectly still, looking straight ahead while Tej Singh waited on his knee, his head bowed. The entire durbar fell silent. Then I saw Sher Singh Attariwala whisper something in the Maharaja's ear. But nothing happened. Duleep locked his hands behind his back and sat down on the throne.

'Well done, my son, may the Guru give you a long life,' Jindan whispered from where she stood behind the purdah, only a few feet from the throne.

That was all that Lawrence needed. He quickly spread the lie that Rani Jindan was an evil influence on her son. He had found the pretext that he had been looking for. Now he could banish her, the queen of Ranjit Singh, from the lion's own kingdom.

But first, they threw me out of Lahore. I was part of the evil influence. They named some others too—Amir Baksh, Har Dayal . . . I was sent away from those lanes where I had seen so much, been part of so many things; sent away to wander from city to city to this day.

Meanwhile, they confined Jindan to the Summan Burj. They took everything away from her, her loyal servants, her jewellery, her wealth, even her son. They thought they would kill her spirit. They knew so little, those firanghis. From her prison, she wrote to Lawrence, and through those who wished her well, the letter came to be known all over Punjab. I remember every word of that letter:

> I had entrusted myself to your care. But you let me be trampled over by traitors. You have not done me justice. You should have instituted an enquiry against me and framed your charges. Instead, you have acted upon the words of traitors. You did not respect the friendship of the Maharaja and you let me be disgraced by others. You did not remain true to treaties and agreements.
>
> Raja Lal Singh was true and loyal to me. You charged him and sent him away but even then I did not say anything to

you. I thought that if the sahib himself is with us, then why fear anyone? I could never imagine that baseless charges would be flung at me and I would be put into prison. Produce, if you can, anything that I have written. Prove any charges levelled against me. Then do as you will.

I, the Maharaja and twenty-two maids are imprisoned in the Summan Burj. All other servants have been dismissed. Our condition is helpless; even water and food are not allowed to us. Why not just hang us instead?

If you give us justice, well and good. Else I shall appeal to London headquarters. Even the promised allowance of a lakh and a half has not been given. I have sold my ornaments to Misr Megh Raj to pay fifty-one thousand rupees that I have spent in the last four months. I have never begged anyone for anything. I have managed by selling my jewellery. Why should you have caused me to be disgraced without a fault? What did poor Mangla do that she too has been turned out?

The Maharaja came to me today and wept bitterly for a long time. Bishen Singh and Gulab Singh have been scaring him, he said. If something were to happen to the Maharaja out of sheer fright, what will I do then? He was told that the sahib had ordered that he was to stay in Shala Bagh and he wept bitterly at that. No other ruler of any kingdom has been treated in this manner.

Why do you take possession of the kingdom through underhand means? Why not do it openly? On the one hand you talk of friendship; and on the other, you have thrown us into prison. Do me justice or I shall appeal to London. You save three or four traitors and put entire Punjab to the sword at their bidding!

She mentioned me in that letter! That still brings tears to these ageing eyes.

But they were not happy with letting her stay in Lahore at all. Currie sahib who had come in place of Lawrence sahib got the senior Sardars to agree with him and sent her away to Sheikhupura, to a jail where they used to keep common criminals.

They took Duleep away to Shala Bagh when they carried her off to Sheikhupura. Mother and son were not to see each for many years after that till he came back from Vilayat to Calcutta, a Christian, an Angrez. I was no longer with her but there were many girls whom I had trained well, so I got news of everything. Like her escape from Chunar fort right under the noses of the sentries. From Chunar she wandered through many cities, gathering the dust of so many villages on her royal feet, disguised as a bairagan . . . She was on the move, always, till she found refuge in the kingdom of Nepal.

How many years she had to stay there—and in such difficult conditions! But at least she was not in the firanghi's hands. She was in exile, not in prison. Every Punjabi heart ached for her, even those that had once plotted against her. Wherever a flame of revolt against the British was lit, it was fanned by the memory of the exiled Maharani, and by pity for her young son.

Duleep Singh, autumn 1893, Paris

They sent my mother away because I did her bidding, because I refused to put the saffron mark on the forehead of that ugly pock-marked Tej Singh as he knelt before me. He is a scoundrel and a traitor, she had said, and should not be rewarded. So I just folded my arms behind my back and that was it. I can be quite stubborn when I need to be. I learnt later from the India Office papers that Henry Lawrence had thought that I showed more intelligence than most English children of my age would have. He forgot that most English children are not kings. Royal blood ran in my veins. And much good that royal blood has done me!

The day they took me away from Bibiji, they sent me on an excursion to Shalimar Bagh and gave me a new mechanical toy. A bird which could be wound up with a key and then it would flutter its red, green and yellow wings so fast that they became a blur. I had never seen that kind of a bird before. I was convinced that it must be an English bird. That is the English sense of justice and fair play, a toy for a kingdom, a toy for a mother. When they told me that she was no longer in Lahore, I replied: 'At least I still have this bird . . .' And they thought their justice had worked, that I was happy.

That is all I have got from the English all my life—toys, playthings, baubles. I got gifts from Dalhousie, including a Bible. I got pampering from Queen Victoria. I got a neat little estate of my own—smaller than a neighbourhood in Lahore—with all the trappings of British nobility—shooting . . . parties . . . London clubs. Yes, I liked it all. I liked all the toys that I got, ever since that bird I was given in Shalimar Bagh. I was an obedient child, and I learnt well to be a reasonable man, a modest little man. I learnt not to be a nuisance and to show gratitude for being put on a leash and fed well. They say I am the lion's son. What would my father have made of me?

And Bibiji . . . I missed her when they took me back from Shalimar Bagh. I refused to stay without her in Summan Burj so they moved me to some rooms above the takhtgah. One day I received a letter from her with some parrots and sweets. And then nothing more.

I did not know then what all she went through. Only when I was in Fattehgarh did I come to know that she had escaped to Nepal. I received a letter or two through her network of agents and I yearned for the day when I could meet her. I found out all the details fourteen years later when I was reunited with her in Calcutta. And then, much after she died, I read her letters in the Punjab papers in the library. I could feel her anguish, her frustration at being separated from me. All mothers and sons feel the same way, even though they may be queens and kings. But letters to Englishmen don't result in much; I should know, I have written so many in the last thirty years.

'You have been very cruel to me,' she wrote from her prison in Sheikhupura fort to John Lawrence who was then acting as Resident. 'You have snatched my son from me. For ten months I kept him in my womb and then I brought him up with great difficulty. Without any fault of mine, you separated me from him. You could have imprisoned me, dismissed my men, turned out my maids. You could have treated me any way you liked but you should not have separated me from him. In the name of the God you worship, and in the name of the King whose salt you eat, restore to me my son. I cannot bear the pain of this separation. Else put me to death. He is very young, incapable of doing anything. I have left my kingdom; I have no need of it. For God's sake, pay attention to my appeals. I have no one to look towards. I will not raise any objections. My son is alone. He has no brother, no sister, no uncle, old or young. He has lost his father. To whose care shall I entrust him? Why is such cruelty being done to me when I am innocent?

'I shall reside in Sheikhupura and shall not go to Lahore. Send my son to me. I will come to Lahore on the days you hold the durbar. I will send him to you on those days. A great deal of injustice has been done to me, to my son. You have accepted what others said. Now put an end to it. Too much has already been done.'

When I read that letter, the dread of those dark days, the sinister tones of the attendants, the loneliness of long evenings in Shalimar Bagh come back to me. And the frustration of a life that was taken away from me comes out in tears. But there must be something wrong with me, that I so easily take the path of tears. Would Ranjit Singh ever have been proud of me? Of a son who has been left with only the loneliness and darkness of this room and with not even the strength to walk to the door? But somewhere I am not all lost; I cannot be. I still have my pride, I still have it, even after my own blood has wounded it.

Arur Singh, winter 1905, Lahore fort

I am, I think, a man of peace; more a diplomat, if you will, than a soldier. But I have known anger. There was a moment when it was close to rage. It happened the day Duleep Singh, my Maharaja, told me the truth about how the British finally took our Punjab. He had been poring over all the papers and copies of the treaties he could find in the libraries and archives in London. Then all the pieces came together.

It was late in 1847 or perhaps early 1848. Slowly, but very surely, the firanghi was tightening the noose around Punjab. Rani Jindan may have gained the moral authority but she was far away. The Regency Council was a collection of quavering, handpicked men. The British Resident and garrison were a permanent feature of Lahore.

But still the new Governor General, the young, the ambitious, the avaricious Marquis of Dalhousie, must have had much to think about. The treaties of 1846 obliged the British to look after their nine-year-old ward, Duleep Singh. The Lahore durbar was still paying twenty-two lakh every year so that the British would ensure peace in Punjab. What excuse could there be for annexation, for looting Lahore's riches? Even Dalhousie knew that the excuse should sound fair to the British Parliament and people. That nation's great arrogance comes from the confidence that on paper everything can be shown to be fair. Reason is worshipped there, for it allows for treachery so well constructed, so calibrated and so precisely and patiently executed, that it becomes an exercise in justice.

The opportunity finally presented itself. The Governor of Multan, Mulraj, resigned from his post. In the early summer days of 1848, two British officers, Vans Agnew and Anderson, went to take over power only to be murdered by some hot-blooded warriors. The mutiny of Multan had begun, with Mulraj as its reluctant leader. Dalhousie saw his chance. The local rebellion, which could have been easily put down by a show of British strength, was allowed to fester. British troops could not be sent to help control the situation, Dalhousie said, because the weather was too hot! Meanwhile, it was made out that the Lahore durbar was inciting the rebels. The irony, of course, was that the ineffectual Lahore durbar was fully loyal to the British and under their protection.

Sensing that treachery was afoot and the loss of their homeland, and their own positions of power, was imminent, the Attariwala Sardars—father Chatar Singh and son Sher Singh—unfurled their flags against the British. Quickly Dalhousie concluded that the 1846 treaties no longer bound him. According to him, the Sikhs had rebelled and the Lahore durbar had not acted against the rebels. There was sufficient ground for annexation. Of course, he chose to forget that it was the British who were treaty bound to ensure peace—that was what they were being paid for every year.

The firanghi then marched into Punjab in full strength. The Attariwalas prepared to hold them at the Chenab, the dark river.

And once again, in the lanes of Lahore, as Mangla Mai told me, it was time for Shah Mohammed, the poet, to dip his pen in ink:

The guns are booming once again, their roar shakes the earth from the Jhelum to the Chenab. The Singhs have wounded the

British lion at Ram Nagar. They exult over his captured
cannon; they laugh at his flag.

Attariwala has moved across the Chaj doab; he watches
the British, with the Jhelum to protect his back. The Sikhs look
for positions in the thorny ravines. They do not like to meet the
British redcoats on the open plain.

Chilianwala will live as long as the history of valour. What
a battle was fought. Cannonball and shot fall like hail, bayonet
clashes with sword, as if there can be no tomorrow.

The laats will remember the day, London will wail for
many months. Two thousand and more of theirs have been
killed. Man upon man, they lie in the nullah and khud. The
Sikhs should not have let them go. But three days and three
nights, the heavens sent rain.

And at Gujerat, on a beautiful and sunny day, the tide has
turned. The Sikh guns boomed for many hours but the laat's
guns won the day. And when the guns were silent, the gora
soldiers slaughtered the ghorcharhas. The drums of the Khalsa
can be heard no more. The Attariwala Sardars have laid down
the sword.

Truly, O Shah Mohammed, Ranjit Singh mar gaya.

Yes, Mangla Mai said to me as she recalled those days: the Sarkar
was now truly dead.

Duleep Singh, autumn 1893, Paris

I have some memories of the day I signed away my kingdom. I
remember waiting at the gate of the fort for Dalhousie's secretary,
Sir Henry Elliott, along with the senior members of the durbar. We
then rode in a procession to the takhtgah. There, while I sat on the
throne for the last time, Dalhousie's secretary read out a long
statement in English to the full durbar. Then it was read out by a
court official in Persian and in Hindustani. I do not think I
understood what was happening. I remember Dewan Deena Nath
stand up and speak in a quivering voice, tears in his eyes, saying that
I should be allowed to stay on the throne, that Punjab should be
restored to me, like France had been to the French.

'Keep quiet,' Elliott told him, 'or you will be sent to Kala Pani.'

Then a document was passed around and I saw the ministers sign it one by one—Deena Nath, Tej Singh, the Fakir. Then it was presented to me. My confidential servant Mian Kheema whispered that I should sign it, so I did too. That was all. After that I knew things were different. People stopped giving me the importance they used to earlier. I do not remember much else. It was all so long ago. The colours of Lahore are fading.

Arur Singh, winter 1905, Lahore fort

These ramparts of red stone that I can reach for and touch with my hands have been mute witness to so much. Henry Elliott must have felt a sense of deep satisfaction as he watched the British flag go up on these very ramparts to the salute of British artillery. He had earned the genuine appreciation and praise of his superior, the Governor General. He had helped put into effect all that Dalhousie had planned, all that Hardinge had put away for later. It did not matter to him that a young prince, whom the British had solemnly promised to protect in his minority, was being deposed by them, that they were blaming their own ward for misrule after having committed, through signed treaties, to help him rule.

The prince, our Maharaja, barely ten years old then, could not have understood that while his advisers would retain their estates, all his privileges were being taken away. His property and immense wealth, including the Koh-i-noor diamond, were confiscated. He was promised a pension of twelve thousand pounds per annum, to terminate on his death.

And he was to be exiled from Punjab.

Book Three

DECEPTION

John Login, autumn 1863, Felixstowe

I have mixed feelings about the 29th of March 1849, the day that Duleep and his Royal Councillors signed the second Treaty of Lahore and the Terms of Annexation that made Punjab ours forever.

The weeks and months before that had not been easy. The winter had been full of battle. I had fought the Sikh rebels with all the strength the good God had invested in me. I had helped in laying out the guns and as a medical officer I had also tended to the wounded, including the Sikhs. After those fierce battles, I would set off with a few native horsemen carrying some water and brandy. Sometimes we would find an occasional Sikh soldier, still proudly clinging to his musket or spear. I would not shoot him down but talk to him, tell him to hand over his arms and come with me. My fellow Englishmen made no secret that they did not think it very wise to help the Sikh wounded this way but I would say that the only way of pointing out the difference between Christians and others was by showing mercy and kindness to one's enemies. So I would pick up the wounded, treat them on the spot or carry them to the nearest hospital. It was no strange act in my view. We, after all, were in a very odd position in that country. According to the Bhyrowal treaty we were supposed to be representatives of the Lahore durbar and yet we were fighting the soldiers of the same durbar.

In March that year, weary from all the fighting that I had seen, I went to Jullunder to be with my old friend, Henry Lawrence. He was then busy making plans for Punjab. The Multan rebellion was pretty much done. Mulraj was in prison and the Attariwala Sardars were being brought to Lahore after surrender. Forty-one guns and sixteen thousand arms had been surrendered across the Jhelum.

'There is a lot of work yet to be done, John,' Lawrence told me one evening as we sat with our tea tray on the veranda of his bungalow. 'I am afraid, impolitic though it may be, the Governor General is set on annexation. It will happen soon.'

I knew that he shared my ambivalence about the annexation. It was not easy to pretend that there was nothing wrong in deposing a young prince who was supposed to be under our protection. I shared none of the exultation that Henry Elliott had shown the day he got the Terms signed and sometimes I feel that Duleep's anger and bitterness that I have begun to see now, began that day.

'I have already been asked to be the Commissioner of the new State,' Lawrence continued. 'There is a role for you too, which you will know in the fullness of time.'

I was to know very soon. I had been recommended very strongly by the Lawrence brothers to be the Superintendent of the young Maharaja after the annexation. They believed that I was the fittest man for the purpose. And when I heard of it, I decided, as was my wont, that I would let the matter be decided by the One who was our Maker, wiser than any of us could ever be.

Killah-ka-Malik, custodian of the Fort! Pension Paymaster! Keeper of the State Treasury, the famous toshakhana! In charge of the stud farms, the artillery workshops, the harems! Guardian of Maharaja Duleep! I was all of these.

I had been chosen to do so many jobs and I was humbled. The Lord was testing his child. I would have to listen to my inner voice and that of my Lord at every step. I knew that I had been chosen because I had always held the distinction between right and wrong dear to my heart. And as never before, I would have to do the right thing in all matters now.

And temptations there were many. That toshakhana—I can never quite forget my first sight of it. Room after room of the most precious items; a world of gold and silver, relics of great value to the Sikhs, platefuls of jewels casually wrapped in muslin, several gold thrones, pile upon pile of intricately embroidered cashmere shawls, royal armour, weapons, tents and silver tent poles, saddles encrusted with large precious stones. And of course, the centrepiece of it all, the Koh-i-noor, the mountain of light, the symbol of power and glory. Still uncut, the diamond was mounted with two others in an armlet that the kings used to wear. The sight of that diamond itself was enough reward for the hard work that had gone into the annexation of Punjab. When it reached Her Majesty, as Dalhousie immediately decided it should, any doubts about the rectitude of what had been done would surely be stilled. All that was handed over to me without a list, without a statement. That was proof enough, I concluded humbly, of the high regard that my integrity enjoyed with Dalhousie and Lawrence.

But statements had to be made, of each and every item, to the last degree. It was not just my sense of order that dictated my actions, but also a desire to ensure that not the slightest blemish devolved on my name. The young Maharaja even sent me three Arab horses one day and of course I was then obliged to choose one of them to ride. But still I decided to purchase a horse of my own. Too scrupulous, everybody thought. Perhaps. But I felt happy in my independence.

I also had to decide what could be kept for the Maharaja's use and all else was to be appropriated. And while all this was being done, I had to politely handle the curiosity of all and sundry, especially the wives of the senior British officers who were dying for a glance at the riches that had suddenly become ours.

Sometimes, especially when I glance at the copy of the memorandum that is still with me, I wonder at myself and thank the Lord for the strength and forbearance that he granted me:

Memorandum of Memorabilia, under charge of
John Spencer Login
In the Citadel of Lahore, April 6th, 1849.

The young Ruler of the Sikhs,
The Families of Runjeet Singh and of all the successive Maharajahs of
*   the Punjab, including thirty-three Ranees and 130 concubines*
The Princes of the Abdalee family, rulers of Afghanistan and Cashmere
The Court Establishment of all the Lahore Maharajahs, including six
*   sets of courtesans, natives of Cashmere, and five full bands of*
*   musicians*
The Nawabs of Mooltan and their families
State prisoners

Moolraj, ex-Nazim of Mooltan

Rajah Chuttar Singh

Rajah Shere Singh

Rajah Lal Singh

And ten other men of note, including Hakim Rai and his two sons

The female attendants of Ranee Jindan, from Chunar

The keys and royal Seals of the Motee Mundir and of Govindgur (royal treasuries)

The diamond (Koh-i-Noor)

The state jewels and treasures in gold, silver, and precious stones; dishes, plates, cups, cooking pots, and gurrahs of gold and silver

The vast store of cashmere shawls, chogas etc.

Runjeet's golden chair of State, his silver summer house, gold and silver poles; tents and camp equipage of rich cashmere; arms and armour, very magnificent

Shah Sooja's state pavilion, gorgeously embroidered

Relics of the Prophet: his shoes, walking stick, shirt, cap and pyjamas; his book of the prayers in the Kufic character; several locks of his hair

The Kulgee 'Plume' of the last Guru (Gobind)

The sword of the Persian hero Roostum taken from Shah Sooja by Runjeet Singh

The sword of Wuzeer Fatih Khan, founder of the Baruksye family at Cabul and Candahar

The sword of Holkar (an old Spanish blade)

The armour worn by the warriors and the Sirdars of note, many of them stained with their blood

The wedding garment of Maha Singh

Besides these many valuable curiosities and relics of all kinds, too numerous to note

That memorandum, fading in my files, tells a story of its own.

The opulence of my new residence, in sharp contrast to my rough camps in Kabul and Herat, was not the only thing that kept me awake at nights after the annexation. I worried how I would be able to discharge my task regarding the young Maharaja in all its aspects.

And I understood that the price of my new status would perhaps be measured out in sleepless nights. On such nights I wished for Lena's presence at my side. But she was in London and Edinburgh, settling our three eldest children. I needed her then more than ever, her unquestioning support, her quiet wisdom.

On one such night I was standing in the veranda of my chambers, smoking my pipe, lost in some thought. It was a pleasant night, and it seemed a relief just to be outdoors. There was no moon but an unreal luminosity radiated from the white dome of the Badshahi mosque. It reflected faintly from the marble walls of the baradaris across the courtyard, bounced off the neat garden and the central fountain and reached the carved outer pillars of the Shish Mahal. Beyond these pillars, the Mahal lay in darkness but I knew that the walls were encrusted with mirrors and precious stones.

All at once, the sky seemed to open up. The clouds that had gathered all week, like armies that used to amass in the plain beyond the walls of the fort, burst upon us. The wind came rushing in from the Ravi over the ramparts and blew the rain in powerful swathes through Summan Burj. I was about to go indoors when a sudden burst of activity from the Shish Mahal caught my eye. Duleep, in full dress, complete with his turban and pearls, burst forth from between the carved pillars. He ran across the marble floor and splashed into the huge puddles that had already formed in the garden. There, his arms stretched skywards, his palms open to the cascading rain, the young boy stood for a few minutes. Then he twirled and furiously gestured to some companions who stood in the shelter of the verandas. Laughing loudly, he shouted some instructions to them. I could not make out what he was saying; the rain swept away the words.

I was mesmerized by the sight of the boy and his grown-up companions playing in the rain. They didn't seem to have any care in the world. I wondered whether I or any of my countrymen would have been able to give ourselves up with such abandon if we had been in the position that the Sikh king and courtiers were in. A kingdom lost, the Sikh empire ended forever, the British in charge of Lahore and the toshakhana and they could still dance in the rain!

I decided to walk across to the Maharaja's chambers and wait for him to return.

Duleep's face was flushed with joy, his round eyes were sparkling. When he saw me in his chamber he let out a spontaneous burst of laughter.

'What fun, my friend! What bliss! I love to play in the rain. I cannot remember ever seeing such rain.'

'Yes, Your Highness. It is quite a downpour and I am glad you enjoyed yourself.'

'Did you see how they all danced with me? I wish you had come too.'

'No, thank you, Your Highness. I am quite fine as I am. And may I suggest that you change into something dry or you may catch a bad chill.'

Duleep's expression changed suddenly. He threw his head back and placed his hands on his hips.

'I will not change. It is too early to change my clothes.'

'It is early, Your Highness, but you are drenched.'

'I do not care. I will not change my clothes,' said the Maharaja and turning on his heel walked away. But he did not leave the room.

I knew that this was a round that I had to win.

'Your Highness, as someone who has been entrusted with your welfare by the most noble Governor General, I must insist. I will retire to my chamber now and I would be most obliged if Your Highness changed his clothes within the next half an hour. I will be informed accordingly.'

'I said I will not do it,' the Maharaja's resolve seemed unmoved.

'Then, Your Highness, you would be enjoining me to use force.'

There was a silence and only the rain that fell sharp and furious could be heard. I bowed and turning on my heel went into the corridor that led to my chambers. Scarcely had I reached there that the curtain was swept aside and Duleep Singh rushed in through the door that had been specially created to join the two living quarters. He was in tears. Rubbing his eyes with his fist, he looked beseechingly at me.

'This is not fair, what you do to me. You cannot force me on these things. According to the Treaty, I can do as I wish. I am not a prisoner.'

Sobbing into his hands, he sat down on a chair in front of me.

I put a gentle hand on his shoulder and signalled to the attendants to take him away and help him change his clothes.

There was very heavy rain another day too, the day of Duleep's birthday party. I had thought it would be nice if the Residency folk came across to wish the Maharaja. After all, it was the first birthday after the loss of his throne and a little civility and attention shown to him on the occasion would help salve the wound. Despite the heavy rain, it all went well and the next day, as was my habit, I sat in one of my rooms, the room that used to be once occupied by Jawahar Singh, and wrote to Lena:

Citadel, Sep. 5th, 1849

Yesterday was the birthday of the little Maharaja; he is now eleven, and entering his twelfth year.

Everything was done that was in my power, to give the anniversary due honour, so that he should feel the difference in his position as little as possible, and not contrast unpleasantly with the last, when he was a reigning king. No doubt, in spite of all, he did see and feel a great difference, poor little man! But nevertheless he thoroughly enjoyed himself, and was delighted with the fireworks as any boy of his age would be. Luckily the evening was fine, though the deluge of rain in the morning was dreadful, and upset all my grand arrangements.

I had the great pleasure of presenting to the Maharaja, on the morning of his birthday, a lakh of rupees worth of his own jewels from the toshakhana that I had been empowered by the Government to select and present to him.

He appeared, therefore, dressed most splendidly; wearing, besides other jewels, the diamond aigrette and star I had selected. When I congratulated him on his appearance, he innocently remarked that on his last birthday he had worn the Koh-i-noor on his arm!

The rain was so heavy, that to prevent the poor Ranees getting drenched in their finery, I ordered the wall of the Palace to be broken through to admit them direct from their apartments, instead of going round in the rain to the ordinary entrance. They all came early, very smartly got up, to present their nuzzars to their little Sovereign, and to see and speak to him a while, when offering their congratulations. I had purdahs put up to screen the Mohammedan ladies from observation; but the Sikh Ranees are not so particular, and were quite ready to chat with me. The little fellow gave himself up to enjoyment for the rest of the day, like the boy as he is.

I shall be truly glad when it is settled what is to be the future destination of Duleep Singh. Sir Henry and Mansel both advise his being sent to England at once; but Lord D is not fond of suggestions, so we all wait for his decision. Sir Henry says that the Dhoon, with a large estate or jagheer, might not be a bad thing.

Either of these plans would suit me; but if it is decided to send him to some place in Central India, and to bring him up with no other expectation than to be a mere pensioner, debauched and worthless like so many others, then I feel it is no work for me, and I'll wash my hands of the charge, take my furlough, and join you in England; but all this is in wiser hands than mine, and I leave it there contentedly.

The decision that I needed so desperately was made soon enough. Lord Dalhousie, during an inspection visit to Lahore fort in November 1849, told me to prepare to take away Duleep to Fattehgarh on the banks of the Ganges, far away from the Punjab.

When we first moved to Fattehgarh, an ancient Sikh retainer who had attached himself to the party that came with us made an unholy commotion on the first evening there. 'Oh you firanghis! To what a miserable, hot place have you flung our Duleep!' he kept crying. And at first glance, his complaint was understandable. Fattehgarh camp had grown around the remnants of a mud fort and three villages. A small settlement of civilian Englishmen and indigo planters lived their lives around the theatre with its tamarind tree and the Grecian church with its spire. And when they died of malaria, cholera or the heat they were buried in the two cemeteries shaded with neem and shisham trees. The Ganges ran nearby and when the water was low, the villagers planted melons on the banks. The manure attracted endless swarms of flies and mosquitoes that seemed to be forever circling in the skies above.

But Fattehgarh had been home to exiled royalty before. The Mahratta princess, Her Highness Baiza Bai of Gwalior, had stayed in an old indigo factory, behind the walls of which could be seen galloping her two tame rhinos.

Here, I bought, for fifteen hundred rupees, a bungalow built thirty years earlier by an indigo planter, Martin of Shamsabad. The King of Lahore could fly his hawks to his heart's content in the lawns of Martin's kothi. Other houses close by were taken for myself, for the tutor Guise—an ordinary man I had picked up on the way at Meerut to teach Duleep Singh English, arithmetic and general knowledge—and for the manservant Thornton. Not far away was the house for Rani Dukhno, the young and very beautiful wife of the dead Maharaja Sher Singh and her young son Shahzada Shivdeo Singh, who was to be Duleep's companion. Shivdeo Singh was next in line to the throne and Lord D wanted him away from Punjab too. Soon a young English boy, Tommy Scott, would join them as companion and things would move on smoothly in the direction we desired.

I began to work hard to handle the estate of a king who was no longer a king. I had the bungalows repaired, constructed a covered walkway so that Rani Dukhno could go for her bath down to the river, and most important, tightened the security around the estate to keep a watch on any suspicious people who may try to get in touch with the Punjabi servants. It was a time of blessed toil, and I would spend the day watching over the works, riding my chestnut, Hotspur, a muslin pugree tied, frontier style, on my riding helmet!

And in the evenings I wrote letters—and that was not easy for me, ever since a horse had crunched my right thumb. I wrote to let the Governor General know all that was being done, about the Maharaja's health, about his education, about the expenses. Four thousand rupees had been spent on four Arab horses for Duleep, more on his white dresses that he soiled by playing in the gardens, still more on fireworks on various birthdays. And some money of course had to be left aside for charity. The last item gave me some satisfaction; Duleep was given to charity. Already a hundred destitutes in the area were receiving regular help. It seemed such a Christian thing to do. Much better than feeding hordes of Brahmins.

Dalhousie's rebuke to me on the matter of the rewards for the escort on the journey from Lahore to Fattehgarh brought home to me Duleep's reality. A selection of the best men—the Governor General's Bodyguard, Skinner's 'Canaries', men of the 6th Light Cavalry, 18th European infantry, 50th Native Infantry and Horse Artillery—had accompanied us from Lahore. They were to guard us against any attempt by any bunch of desperadoes to rescue the Maharaja. The men had done their duty well, riding alongside the Maharaja whether he rode on his elephant in the forenoons or in his carriage in the afternoons. And once camp was made, European sentries would watch his bed all night. And so we had come through Ferozepur, Ambala, Saharanpur, Meerut. Not the slightest threat was allowed to rear its head. Besides, the men had shown great civility and attention to the young Maharaja during the march.

When the time finally came for them to leave, Duleep said that he wanted to give presents to the officers and men. I saw nothing wrong with that, to be honest, it being hardly likely that these circumstances would be repeated too often. Captain Hampton, the Commanding Officer, and Captain Thomson, the Commander of the detachment of the Governor General's Bodyguard, got very handsome swords with gold handles and gold scabbard mounting. Some of the junior officers got swords with gilt handles or finger rings studded with a ruby or a diamond or emerald. Another five hundred rupees were handed over to Captain Hampton to buy sweetmeats for the men of the detachment.

But when I wrote to the Governor General recommending that the officers be allowed to retain their gifts, the sharp response brought a flush to my face.

'The rules of the Court are peremptory on this subject,' wrote Dalhousie, 'and rightly so.' The officers must submit the gifts to the toshakhana or pay for them. And as for me, I should not recommend, 'the giving of presents by the boy' and should stick to the rules of the company.

I understood. Dalhousie could refer to Duleep as His Highness and as easily turn around and refer to him as a boy. Dalhousie too had his orders from the Secret Committee, which had recorded, I came to know later: '. . . *Maharajah Duleep Singh should be treated with kindness and consideration, but be well watched, and not raised into more importance than really attached to him.*'

How much importance could really attach, I wondered, to a boy who was also a king, but a king without a kingdom?

It was not going to be easy. I wanted Lena to join me as soon as possible. I wrote to her:

Fattehgarh, March 6th, 1950

I shall be glad when you join me, for I cannot expect to have more than two or three years in which we can influence the young Maharajah's mind favourably towards our domestic life and I must not lose them on any account. He will have an opportunity of seeing how we live in our homes, and he will be one of us, and will look upon you as a mother, and respect and esteem you . . . I was so pleased with the Maharajah on the occasion of the grand day of the Hoolie festival. He showed such self-denial and self-restraint in not exhibiting any desire to participate in the undignified and, indeed, objectionable frolics of the people, that I arranged something more harmless for him in the evening, to his great enjoyment and delight. The large centre rooms are splendid places for hide-and-seek, blind-man's buff etc. All these games are new to him and the Shahzadah. Imagine the scene! The ruler of the Sikhs, the young Shahzadah, Sirdar Boor Singh Butaliwallah, Dewan Ajoodea Pershad, Fakeer Zehoorudin, Mr Guise, Mr Barlow and myself, all engaged in the game. The Maharajah's shouts of glee ringing all over the place as each was caught in turn. I was glad indeed that you sent him that book of games, The Boy's Own Book.

Duleep Singh, autumn 1893, Paris

When we left Lahore, I was not told where we were going. But I was full of foreboding because of the way the women in the palace wailed and cried as the procession left the fort, like they had when the funeral processions of my brothers had passed. I prayed silently as we passed my father's memorial.

It was a long journey and I was often sad. But I was glad that at least Shivdeo and his mother, two members of my family, were with me. Login tried his best to keep us happy and occupied. At Ambala the Commanding Officer organized a party at his house in my honour. I remember wondering why the English sang as they did, as if they were in pain, and I blushed when I saw them dancing, holding their women and twirling them around. I had never seen such things before.

In Fattehgarh I was completely in Login's hands. He went with me everywhere or left a hawaldar close to me. Outside the compound of my house, there were always soldiers on guard though within the gardens I could do as I wished—run around, paint, ride my horse or learn my lessons. On some days Login would make a special effort to entertain me. Like the fireworks on the river bank that he ordered on Shivdeo's birthday. My yacht was rigged up to look like a ship. All illuminated, it moved up and down the river all the while that the party was going on and gave everybody a great sense of delight.

The early morning rides around Fattehgarh used to be exciting too—for Shivdeo and me as well as for the villagers, for I would ride out in full state, followed by my Sikh attendants in their fine shirts and turbans and of course the Governor General's Bodyguard in scarlet uniforms and Skinner's Irregulars in saffron. Sometimes I would ride on an elephant but mostly it was in my carriage drawn by four Arab greys.

Yet I could not help feeling that I was a prisoner.

John Login, autumn 1863, Felixstowe

The matter of the Maharaja's attendants had worried me right from the start. When leaving Lahore my main preoccupation in that regard had been that they should be all men of the highest fidelity. I had in fact asked Duleep to himself select them along with me. When he told them that he was leaving Punjab, many of the Sikh attendants dropped out. Even amongst those who came, many of the

Punjabi servants were keen to return and I saw no reason to discourage them. I thought that was indeed better: the possibility of their being approached one way or the other by Jindan or some other intriguers could not be ruled out. So I brought up many of my old Lucknow retainers. The day that Mian Kheema, the Mohammedan attendant who had been with Duleep since his birth, decided to go back to Lahore, I knew that a trustworthy replacement had to be found. Bhajan Lal was highly recommended. He was a young Brahmin of excellent moral character and had studied at the American Mission school at Farrukhabad. Of course he could write and speak fairly good English, but what was more, as I discovered soon, he had a commendable depth of conviction on religious matters and a deep sympathy for our faith, though he continued to adhere to all the ceremonial observances, in matters of food and clothing, of a Brahmin.

Duleep Singh, autumn 1893, Paris

Now that I think of it, Bhajan Lal was a clever man. A very pleasant man too, from what I can remember. I think Login selected him to look after me because he spoke English. And those days, soon after we had reached Fattehgarh, I was very keen to speak English like Tommy Scott and Robby Carshore, sound not so much like a native prince but an English sahib. I wanted to be like them in so many other ways too, have their uncomplicated carefree attitude, play cricket and football like they could, even get into the kind of clothes that they wore—shorts and shirts and stockings. Once Login suggested that I should have another Indian boy as playmate, besides Shivdeo. I don't know why he thought that was necessary, but in any case, I would have none of it. Tommy and Robby were fine with me; if there were more such boys that too would be fine, but I did not want Indian boys. They could not, I felt, be my equals, at my lessons or on the field. I was their king still, even if I had signed the Terms of Annexation. That was for the British, not between my people and me.

Mian Kheema had been different from Bhajan Lal. I remember him today only as a hazy presence through my fatigue and weakness.

In these smudged memories, Mian Kheema is quietly carrying me,
putting me on a horse, helping me dress, putting food in front of
me, talking to me as I fall to sleep.

And then soon after we reached Fattehgarh, he left for Lahore.
I wonder, did he want to leave me or was that too part of the plan?
He had been with me since I was born and surely, his loyalty to me
could not have changed simply because I had been taken away from
Lahore. I needed him, he must have known that, but still he left.
God knows what they said to him, Login and the others. Perhaps
they refused him permission to bring his family from Lahore, or told
him that he was no longer needed since he could not speak English,
that he would be useless to me as I became more English than
Indian, as I learnt to read and write, as I began to move away from
what I was, as I began to read the Bible ... Perhaps in their minds,
perhaps in Login's mind, or Dalhousie's, or in some dispatch of the
Secret Committee this plan was already in place. And if that was so,
then the reason for Mian Kheema's return to Lahore is clear to me:
he could not read the Bible to me like Bhajan Lal would.

I first came across the scriptures in a little book that was meant
for my lessons—*The English Instructor*.

'Will reading those pages make me a Christian?' I asked Bhajan
Lal.

'Please read them if you wish, Maharaja. All I know is that they
are from the Holy Bible.'

And then every night he read the Bible to me. A chapter or two
as I lay in bed, just before falling to sleep, in his gentle sweet voice.
It kept me from thinking of my mother and from wondering why I
had been separated from her.

That voice comes back to me now as I lie in this bed preparing
to fall into eternal sleep. I wish someone would come and read me
something to soothe my soul, and I would not care if it was the Bible
or the Guru Granth or even the fantastic tales from the Hindu
shastras ... I have believed in everything and nothing, I have been
Sikh, Christian and Sikh again. Sometimes I feel that I have no
conviction at all.

I urged Bhajan Lal to read to me every day. Unlike the stories
told by the Pandit, Bhajan Lal's stories made me see no gods and

demons outside the window in the dark, among the fragrant flower
bushes and the fireflies that danced and flew across the lawns.
Everything seemed to make sense, the stories of good and evil, the
truth about the greatness of God and those who believed in Him. I
could understand why Bhajan Lal himself believed in the Bible even
though he continued to say that he was a Brahmin.

He did not come with me when I finally left for England. He
continued to live with his family in Fattehgarh. I was told later, years
later, that he had become a successful maker of tents. I wonder what
he read in the last days of his life, the Bible or the Hindu prayers?

Did he find any way to save his soul?

John Login, autumn 1863, Felixstowe

Lena finally landed in India. I decided to meet her in Calcutta and
bring her back with me to Fattehgarh. It was a long and arduous
journey through difficult country and I did not want her to be
exposed to it alone. Captain Campbell of the 7th Madras Regiment
whom I had left in charge of Duleep's affairs kept me well briefed.
During my stay in Calcutta there had been only one piece of
excitement that he immediately reported to me. Intelligence agents
had spotted three suspicious travellers in the bazaar who had been
heard asking about the Maharaja and had made attempts to talk to
his Hindustani servants. One of them had been heard to say, 'We
have a message from his mother, Rani Jindan.' That set the alarm
bells ringing. Campbell had rushed to the bazaar stopping only to
collect the magistrate on the way since the area fell in the latter's
domain. Quickly they had rounded up the three travellers and taken
them to the police checkpost. A thorough search had revealed
nothing on their persons, no letter or message that could have been
smuggled to Duleep. There had been nothing further to do. The
magistrate ordered his men to ride the three ruffians to the limits of
the district and put them on the road to Pilibhit with a clear warning
that if they were seen in those parts again, they would be put in jail
or shot.

But it was when I reached the camp at Allahabad that I got
Campbell's more important dispatch. Duleep had professed a desire

to embrace our faith. Even while I praised the Lord, I was tense. But
I was not too surprised. I should have seen it coming. More than
once, Duleep had remarked on the fantastic and incredible stories
that the Pandit read to him from the Hindu shastras. He regarded it
as nonsense and made no secret of his feelings. In fact, he had
written to me just a few days earlier that Bhajan Lal was reading the
scriptures to him and could I not bring back a Bible from Calcutta?
Even earlier, soon after he was joined by Tommy, Duleep had
wanted to learn some hymns. I chose 'Whenever I take my walks
abroad', and to my surprise, Duleep memorized it with alacrity.

My mind went back to an incident that had taken place a few
days before I left for Calcutta. Duleep, along with one or two
attendants, had rushed into my room early one morning. I had been
working at my desk on some matter of the estate. I do not recall how
but the conversation had taken a strange turn.

'Tell me, is the sun really the centre of our solar system?' the
Maharaja had asked.

'Yes, ever since Copernicus proved it to be so.'

'And the moon?'

'The moon goes around the earth, as the earth goes around the
sun.'

'And does the sun eat the moon on some days?'

'Eat the moon? You mean the eclipse?'

'The Pandit said that I should not look up on the day the sun
eats the moon or I will go blind.'

I tried my best to explain the matter to him. I looked around my
desk and picking up a spherical paperweight and, for want of
anything better, a coat button and using the candle to be the sun,
showed the fascinated prince how, roughly speaking, a lunar eclipse
occurred. When I finished, Duleep clapped his hands gleefully and
his eyes shone with the excitement of discovery.

'I have to learn all these things. Imagine if I learn all about these
things, how stupid the Pandit will feel!'

I did not say anything to that, not wanting to be seen as sowing
any dissent between the Maharaja and his traditional guides. His
feelings had been clear to me but yet his announcement that he
wanted to become a Christian was a little sudden.

This is Campbell's dispatch, part of my journals from those years:

I was sitting in the sun the other day, having finished the morning's work, when young Tommy walked up to me. He was clearly excited about something.

'Excuse me, Captain Campbell, but there is something I have been asked to tell you.'

'Asked to tell me?'

'By the Maharaja.'

'Go ahead.'

'He's told me to tell you that he no longer believes in what the Pandit tells him, that he wants to become a Christian.'

'What do you mean? What are you saying, Tommy?'

'Captain, that is what he told me, he wants to become a Christian. He told me to tell you that.'

'I will come in a few minutes. You may go back to your work. Thank you.'

'Actually, sir, he had told me this some time back, almost a month, but at that time he had made me promise that I would tell no one.'

'I see. Right, Tommy, thank you.'

When I met Duleep Singh, he seemed to be expecting me to come and question him. He answered all my questions with a rebellious deliberation.

'Yes, Captain, what Tommy told you is right. I would now like to become a Christian. I have been thinking about it for some time. I have been listening to the Bible that is being read to me by Bhajan Lal. The Pandit tells me lies. The things he talks of never happen.'

'Right, Your Highness,' I said, making sure I spoke only in Hindustani. Though Duleep has been progressing well in his English under Guise, I did not want to miss out any nuance. 'We will surely talk about all this when Dr Login comes back.'

I am aware, Dr Login, that you want me to keep things quiet till your return, to ensure that there is no public declaration or any obvious change in the Maharaja's way of life, but unfortunately, it was already too late. Almost immediately, the news spread through the camp from the servants to the soldiers and inevitably to Shahzada and Rani Dukhno, the courtiers, the Pandit, and I could feel the tension over the entire establishment.

My intelligence informs me that they all met at night, in the house of the treasurer of the Toshakhana, Missar Ram Kishen. They sat around an oil lamp, much in the nature of a war council. The Pandit, Jawahar Singh the storekeeper, Dewan Singh the carpenter, the orderlies Gurmukh and Shiv Ram, the bearers Ram Singh and Santa, the cook Saudagar and the khidmatgar Jewindah, one of Duleep's favourites. They were all tense and clearly felt the need to do something. I was given a detailed account by our informer among them.

The Pandit was holding his head in his arms.

'These Godless Englishmen have turned the Maharaja's head. This is a disaster,' he said at last. 'He doesn't want to talk to me, he was so angry the other day when I asked him to give away money on Sankrant.'

'I have seen it at close quarters,' Jewindah, the khidmatgar, spoke up. 'I have seen how the black magic has been worked, slowly. He is after all a child. If you say anything to a child in the right way, he begins to believe it.'

'What do you mean? Tell us what you have seen,' the treasurer asked.

'That Bhajan Lal is a Brahmin only in name. He has always lived with the Christians, that is how he learned to speak English. He has been reading every night to the Maharaja from the book of the Christians. God alone knows what he has been reading. I cannot understand a word. But the Maharaja listens, asks him to repeat, asks him to explain. Every night for the last so many weeks.'

'And when I try to read to him,' the Pandit chimed in, 'he turns me away. He laughs at me. Humbug, he told me, all that is written in the shastras is humbug!'

'Pandit, the Maharaja is right, your shastras are humbug.'

Everybody turned to the bearer Ram Singh. The Sikh was

drunk, my spy says, his eyes were red. 'Mumbo-jumbo, that's what you have been telling him, that's why this has happened. You tell him of kings who gave away ten thousand cows in charity every day, you tell him of things that never happened. The Maharaja is a Sikh, he should be told of our Gurus, of what they have written, of what we are.'

'Then why don't the Sikhs teach him? Why didn't even one of your granthis from Lahore come with their Sikh Maharaja? Why was even the Granth not sent? All of them sitting safely in Lahore, enjoying their jagirs.'

'There is no point fighting with each other. Hindus and Sikhs are like lips and the tongue,' the treasurer soothed the atmosphere. 'We are of the same people. Our history, our beliefs are the same. What happens between us remains within us. But if the Maharaja becomes a Christian, all will be lost, his culture, the heritage of his forefathers, his caste, his hope of ever ruling Punjab again.'

Dewan Singh, the carpenter, spoke. 'That is what they want, to finish off every sign of the kingdom of the Sikhs. Let us do something.'

'Kill that fake Brahmin Bhajan Lal first,' Ram Singh spoke again, his long beard shaking with anger in the light of the lantern.

'That is not the way,' the treasurer intervened. 'We should prepare an urzee to the sahib. And then let us all sign it and give it to him. Let us tell them what all this means to us and tell them to stop it from happening.'

I only allowed Ram Kishen to meet me. He came in with folded hands but I could see the resentment in his eyes.

'What is it?' I asked him.

'An urzee, huzoor. From all of us.'

'What is it about?'

'This is a humble request, sahib. You can stop a great injustice from happening. The Maharaja is young, he is but an innocent child. If his steps falter, you can hold his hand and guide him.'

'You have the urzee?'

'Ji, huzoor.' The treasurer extended his hands with the rolled-up piece of paper.

'I will read it. You can go.'

Ram Kishen bowed and moved out of the room. At the door he hesitated, then turned to look at me. For a moment our eyes met. I fear that he was greatly disturbed.

I examined the copy of the urzee that was enclosed with Campbell's dispatch. On the last page there were ten thumb impressions with the names inscribed below. Some of them I had always suspected to be up to no good. And finally they had shown their hand. I read the urzee carefully, going through both the Persian original as well as the English translation.

Maharaja Duleep Singh, the urzee said, had by reason of his experience and youth as well as by the intervention of his associates, shown a tendency to depart from the correct display of respect towards his faith. Were he to persist in this tendency, the result would be a greater calamity than the loss already suffered by him, the loss of his kingdom. The servants then went on to appeal to Campbell: even if little importance could be placed on the professions of so young a child, Campbell would have to answer if the Maharaja suffered any eventual failure of faith.

Campbell had acted intelligently and removed all those who had signed the urzee from the Maharaja's presence. They were confined to a separate bungalow. He had set the stage for me to remove them, if I so wished, all in one blow.

Clearly, there was much that awaited us in Fattehgarh. I glanced at Lena's face. She looked tired and drawn after her long voyage and then the hard ride through the country. But I knew she would understand. The news about Duleep Singh's declaration had both surprised and excited her. She had been aware of such a possibility from my letters and had agreed that we should not be held guilty of any such act that could be perceived as interference in the boy's religion. We could not directly preach to him but we would have to rely on our own lives as example, a spiritual, benevolent, healthy example of what a Christian life could be. I was relieved that Duleep's decision had coincided with her return. She would be a great support in all my efforts and Duleep, I was sure, given her kind disposition, would soon grow fond of her; in fact, his letter to me in Calcutta had already enquired warmly about her. We rode on, without tarrying at Allahabad.

Arur Singh, winter 1905, Lahore fort

When the Maharaja decided to return to the faith of his fathers, he told me something of the days when he was shown, cunningly, the road away from perhaps the last thing that bound him to Punjab. The rest I discovered on my own, scrutinizing the papers and letters of the time that the Maharaja had collected.

It took the Englishmen a few weeks to sort things out. It was not a small thing—to handle the conversion of a native prince to Christianity. The men of the East India Company had to be very careful of what people thought of them, how history judged them. All the paperwork had to be complete. The file had to be correct, with all the notings in place. Nothing should show that undue influence had been used, that a position of trust had been abused.

Dalhousie's instructions to Login were clear. A full enquiry had to be conducted into the circumstances of Duleep Singh's declaration and reported to Dalhousie who in turn would report back to the Court of Directors in London. Had anybody, Login, the teachers, the fellow students of the Maharaja, ever talked to Duleep about religion? How had the Bible been obtained? Who had read it out to the Maharaja? And until things were sorted out, there should be no public declaration. Senior courtiers like Ayodhya Prasad and Fakir Zehuruddin should be kept around.

Within a month, the report reached Lord Dalhousie at Fort William, Calcutta. John Login, as usual, had done a thorough job. He had issued memoranda to all the people around Duleep Singh who mattered and their responses now lay before the Governor General. Dalhousie, it is recorded, went through each of them carefully:

Bhajan Lal: *'The Maharaja had noticed some pages containing scriptures behind his course book,* The English Instructor, *and had wanted to read them. I told him, read it if you like. He was always questioning the*

Hindu shastras: what is the use of bathing in the Ganges? If we do wicked things and then go and bathe in the Ganges will we still go to Heaven? He saw the copy of the Holy Bible in my hand and wanted to buy it from me. I do not want to sell it to you, Maharaj, I told him but I will present it to you if you can read a chapter from it without assistance. He did do so and I presented the Bible to him. Then as he wished I read to him, sometimes the Bible, sometimes a few tricks or stories out of the other book he liked so much, the Boy's Own Book. *No Englishman ever talked to him of religion. One Sunday, when I came back after spending a day in the city, the Maharaja told me that he had become a Christian, that he would no longer go out and play on Sunday. But again one Sunday, I saw him go out with his hawk and when I questioned him about this, he apologized, saying he had forgotten.*

Another day, when I came back from the market, I saw him sitting at the table with Tommy and Robby. He himself was boiling water for tea. He told me he would have tea with the English boys; he would thus break his caste. All that he did was out of his own pleasure.'

Walter Guise, the tutor: *'The two boys who studied with Duleep Singh, Tommy Scott and Robby Carshore, had not exerted any influence on the Maharaja. In fact, I am convinced that the Maharaja is not declaring his intention to become a Christian to please any Englishman, otherwise why would he have wanted to hide the fact and wait until he went to England and by the very act of crossing the seas, broke his caste? This is out of his own disposition; even earlier he has remarked that when he grows up, he wants to learn about all religions and then finally choose his own.'*

Dewan Ayodhya Prasad: *'Dr Login had allowed religious freedom to the Maharaja. Only once, before leaving Lahore, had he said that expenditure on alms and ablutions should be controlled and this had pleased everybody. He had asked Sikh granthis to accompany the Maharaja to Fattehgarh but none had wanted to, only the Pandit had come along. All rites and rituals had been observed and the food for the Maharaja had always been cooked the correct way. I heard him once joking with Shahzada Shivdeo, holding up the Bible. On reading this book, he said, one becomes a Christian. Then I shall not read it, replied the Shahzada, and nor shall you. But I have read it, the Maharaja said.*

Then I shall not eat with you, the Shahzada replied. A few days later they were eating together when the Maharaja reminded the Shahzada of the conversation. The Shahzada stopped eating and started crying. The servant Hari Kishen said that the Maharaja is only joking and so did the Maharaja—I am only joking, Shahzada, you need not cry. But sometimes he did not joke. He got angry with servants when they wanted him to perform ablutions. One day the Pandit went to him with some money to offer in puja. The Maharaja flung it down and said that he would not perform puja or make offerings. I did not approve of the way the servant wrote the urzee, that is not the language to use. We are only servants, the Maharaja can decide what he wants to do. That is what I have told the Fakir sahib and Boor Singh also.'

Fakir Zehuruddin Shah: *'It is nobody's fault, nor anybody's doing. Both Login sahib and Campbell sahib are nice men, taking care of the Maharaja, taking care of his health and happiness, education, upbringing, comforts. Login sahib has created this little town for him, designed houses and grounds in a way that the Maharaja does not feel the lack of anything. And they have always been careful that the Maharaja is allowed the full freedom to practise his religion. They have always treated the Pandit well, allowed him to perform his rituals, to offer charities, to feed the poor and the needy. The Maharaja has a strong mind of his own, may Allah bless him. He does not listen to others. He laughs at superstition, questions the things that the Pandit tells him and there is none who can remonstrate. One of the servants had the foolish courage to talk to him about it, urging him not to refuse religious offerings on the day of Sankrant. The Maharaja took umbrage, shot back in anger that he knew what to do and what not to do, that he would no longer be fooled by empty meaningless rituals of the Hindu Pandit. I am afraid that the Pandit's days with him are numbered. In fact I myself have heard the Maharaja say one day: "When he returns from Gaya, I will discharge him." The servants are angry, they are bitter, they feel that he has been led on, his mind has been turned by the sweet-talking Englishmen. But I know my place; my place is not to remonstrate. In fact, I think after the discussion that we, the Dewan sahib, Boor Singh and I, had with Campbell sahib yesterday, he did the right thing by having all the servants who signed that petition locked up in a separate house. It would be easy for any one of them to, Allah forbid, poison the Maharaja's parshad. They after all are the ones who cook and serve him. I am glad I mentioned this possibility to Campbell sahib and that he listened to me. I can only pray for the Maharaja's safety and welfare, the rest is up to him to do as he wishes.'*

Boor Singh: *'I am not a man who has much to say. I listened to what the Dewan sahib and the Fakir sahib said yesterday and I agree with them. It is not our place to question the Maharaja's views or to protest in the way that the illiterate servants have done. They are villagers, roughnecks. They easily forget their place, begin to think that since the Maharaja is but a child, they can question what he plans to do. I am steeped in the culture of the Lahore court. I have served it for so many years. My job is to agree with the wishes of my Sovereign, to serve him to the utmost of my capabilities. But I do not believe that Login sahib is to be faulted. He always let the Maharaja fulfil all his religious inclinations and obligations. In fact, even after reaching Fattehgarh, he has made all the arrangements that were necessary for the fulfilment of the religious obligations of the royal family. We have all seen it. Whenever the Maharaja or Shahzada Shivdeo or his mother, the Rani ji, have wanted to bathe in the holy waters of Ganga ji, Login sahib has immediately given orders that tents be pitched on the banks of Ganga ji to enable them to do so.'*

Yes, the file looked very good. It would be difficult for anyone, including Duleep, to ever think that he had become a Christian under the influence of the Englishmen.

John Login, autumn 1863, Felixstowe

I went to all possible lengths to make sure that nobody blamed me for proselytizing the young Maharaja. I had banned the use of beef at my table as a general rule. There was to be no smoking around the house. I brought along the reluctant Hindu Pandit from Lahore. The Sikh granthis didn't even pretend that they wanted to come. I made all the right noises. I told them that there would be a proper place in Fattehgarh for the Holy Granth and even during the several weeks of the march from Lahore we would ensure its respectful carriage in a separate tent.

But not one of them volunteered. No wonder he knows next to nothing about Sikhism, about the Gurus and their teachings. Instead, he has been told only mythological stories by the Pandit. Besides, and perhaps there one can see the hand of God, he has always had Muslim attendants and advisers around him. For years there was Mian Kheema and the Fakirs Nuruddin and Zehuruddin. They didn't believe in worshipping idols, in praying to the sun and the planets. And I am sure when he began to raise doubts, they must have added their tuppenny worth. In any case, and this he has told me more than once, he hates the ferocity of the Sikhs, their killing and violence. He still has nightmares, poor boy, of the day they killed Jawahar Singh at Mian Mir. This boy was in the wretched Jawahar's arms even as he was being killed.

Ayodhya Prasad and Zehuruddin stayed through those early months—Dalhousie had indicated that I try to keep them—and when they finally left for Lahore much later in the year, they were handsomely rewarded. The Dewan was even given a horse by the Maharaja. But the servants were another story. I asked many of them to leave, especially among the group that had signed the petition. There was some unhappiness about that step in the Company. Dalhousie let me know that I had not done too well in sending so many people back. They would carry tales to Lahore about how they had been sent back for trying to save the faith of their Maharaja from the firanghi. But I felt that these tales would be told anyway. If we had to ensure that the Maharaja grew up in the manner that we wanted, then it was better to rid his household of people who were constant reminders of his past and his legacy. Such ideas would make him very difficult to handle once he came of age and became his own master.

Some of the servants stayed on, despite their signatures on the petition: the treasurer Ram Kishen, the storekeeper Jawahar Singh, the cook Saudagar and a bearer.

In any case, that report did the trick, as far as we were concerned. The Governor General replied that he was quite satisfied that no undue influence had been used on the boy by any of the Englishmen around. True, Bhajan Lal had been reading the Bible to him, but we could scarcely be blamed for that. I conveyed the Governor General's satisfaction to Campbell and Guise so as to set their minds at rest.

Dalhousie also had ideas of how we should handle the matter thereafter. The most important thing of course was that we shouldn't make too much of a fuss about it. As he wrote: 'We are labouring for good; do not trumpet your labours in anticipation of your success.'

I told Duleep as much, in different ways.

'Your Highness, you have to understand the gravity of your step and whatever we do further has to be with your full understanding. I would request that, at the present time, you should carry on as you have been doing so far so that your caste and other religious obligations are fully observed. Of course, if you like, you may continue to read the Holy Book.'

He too was not one given to fuss and readily acquiesced in what I said. In fact, he made things easier by refraining from attending prayers at my home with the family, as he had been doing for some time.

'I cannot be hypocritical,' he said. 'I do not understand what is being said. I don't know enough English.'

He continued to read the scriptures though and would usually ask Guise or Bhajan Lal to explain passages to him. He was keen to learn, of that I had little doubt. But his good sense was hampered first by the natural indolence of his character and additionally by the hot season that stretched for months in Fattehgarh. He knew that and would often try to shift the blame on me for not pushing him hard enough to apply himself to his lessons.

'Please insist,' he once said, in the days when he was trying to gain knowledge of the English language and the scriptures at the same time, 'that I pay attention to my lessons. I know that is good for me. Otherwise I shall blame you hereafter if I am not well instructed like an English gentleman.'

Duleep Singh, autumn 1893, Paris

Perhaps if I had not been so keen to do everything they wanted, my life may have turned out different. Perhaps I should have shown more resistance to reading the Bible or learning the English language or dressing up like an English gent. But I was ever ready to oblige in those days. It is good to remember that when I get so worked up about things now.

John Login, autumn 1893, Felixstowe

Soon the clearance for further action arrived. Guise's burden of educating Duleep was to be shared by Reverend Carshore, the Government Chaplain. He was a discreet man; it was important that Duleep's conversion not become some sort of celebrated case to be discussed in religious periodicals.

Twice a week, the Reverend would visit him and explain the ways of God. My good wife and I would swell with pride as we saw the young boy engrossed in his lessons almost in our own household. By a happy chance we had witnessed how a heart that could have languished forever in darkness had received God's light. Duleep's earnestness, his desire to conform to our ways of life, to be in every way that he could like Tommy Scott and Robby Carshore, was touching.

His desire to go to England was also fully formed by then. He talked of it at every opportunity even when once I tried to ascertain his views on marriage. I must confess that I had been making enquiries regarding the young princess of Coorg, who was being sent to study in England.

'I will think of marriage only after I am eighteen and by that time I will be in England. I will marry there.'

'You really want to go to England, Your Highness?'

'I dream about it. Every night. Even last night I saw England in my dreams. I met Wellington sahib. I went to his house.'

Some day he would go to England, that much I knew. Dalhousie had mentioned the possibility to me even in Lahore. But it would take time. Neither the Governor General nor the Court of Directors thought it to be such a good idea yet. He was but a child yet, uncertain in the English language, caught at a delicate spiritual turn. The Secret Committee in a letter had indeed said that they were 'glad to find that he shows a preference for English studies but we do not wish he should be encouraged in his desire to visit Europe'.

As things turned out, his progress in his lessons, his earnest pursuit of a Christian life crowned by the most glorious moment of his baptism, his determination and my sincere recommendations helped a couple of years later to change their mind.

But back then I had to concentrate on matters at hand: ensuring that he stayed steadfast on the course that he had chosen, hoping that my wife and I and our other Christian brethren would by example convince him of the superiority of our way of life as compared to a life of indolent idleness that pensioned princes in India were wont to live.

And yes, I had also to keep Rani Dukhno and her son in check. After they came to know of Duleep's desire to become a Christian, they had become hosts to a new hope. The Rani was heard telling her confidantes that now that Duleep had lost his caste, her son would be restored as the ruler of the Punjab. I reported that to Dalhousie and it gave me great pleasure to convey his views to the immensely beautiful but uselessly ambitious Rani.

'The Raj of the Punjab is at an end forever,' I told her, 'and any contemplation of the restoration of your son or of anybody else to sovereignty there is a crime against the State.' I hinted at the import of the rest of Dalhousie's blunt instructions. If she carried on, there would be immediate and disastrous consequences. They would be deprived of their stipends and be sent without further notice to the most distant part of India, or more probably beyond the sea to the dreaded Kala Pani. The hint was taken, for all talk of the Shahzada Shivdeo seeking the throne of Punjab stopped. She never forgave me after that. Even when Duleep was leaving for England and wanted to take Shivdeo with him, she wrote a huge complaint to the Governor General against me, accusing me of a host of inequities, of which child-stealing was the least.

Duleep Singh, autumn 1893, Paris

I had been waiting more than a year to get out of Fattehgarh. I hated its yellow blazing heat and its searing hot summer winds. In that heat one could not do much, except stay indoors, trapped in those long hours of lessons through which I barely stayed awake and then sleep through the long afternoons.

The cool freshness of that morning in Hardwar as I stepped out of the huge red and white striped tent was exciting. We were camped close to a thick dark green forest and all around us there was the morning activity of the camp, the lighting of fires, the rolling up of tents, the gradual movement of elephants and horses. We had been on the road for two months, through Agra, Delhi, Meerut, Roorkee ... on our way to the hill station of Mussoorie. I almost felt free. I saw Shivdeo come out of his tent, his face flushed with excitement. It was an even bigger thing for him. He was travelling for the first time without his mother.

'Look at those clouds!' he said.

They were quite a sight. Heavy and dark, they sat low over our camp, waiting to burst.

'I cannot wait for it to start raining,' I replied.

'How will we go if it starts raining?'

'We'll go. We'll just carry on even if we get drenched. But first we will see Hardwar. Dr Login will arrange it, I am sure. Won't you, my friend?' I turned to Login who had just walked out of his own tent and come up to us.

'If you like, Your Highness, but I am not too keen to send the entire procession with the escort and carriage into the crowded parts of Hardwar. We may have to find some other way, if the weather holds, that is,' he said, looking up at the skies.

Dr Login had arranged the entire trip to the hills meticulously. Initially he had tried to dissuade me from my intention to spend the hot season in the hills.

'It will not be an easy journey, Your Highness,' he had said. 'It will involve many weeks on the road. And it would be impossible to ensure in the hills the kind of comforts and conveniences of residence that you are used to in Fattehgarh camp.'

But I had insisted; I had learnt how to tackle him. Again and again I would bring up the possibility in our conversations, reeling out the reasons he would like to hear. It would be nice to have the company of more European boys, my afternoons would not be wasted in lazy sleep, I could add to my collection of birds, I could get some exotic hill plants, I could increase my knowledge about different kinds of insects ... Finally, Login had hinted at the possibility to Dalhousie, indicating also that the ideal choice would be the hill station of Mussoorie. The other alternative, Nainital, would simply not offer the choice of enough European playmates. Dalhousie hadn't been ecstatic about the idea, from what Login told me, but the permissions had finally come in.

The local civil and army officers had arranged things well at all the stations we passed with receptions in our honour. At each place I along with Shivdeo would pay social calls on the local commanding officer and then there would be the return calls. All very pleasant. In Agra, we saw the Fort and the Taj Mahal but the most exciting thing there was a visit to the printing foundry. One visit was not enough; I went a second time to understand how it all worked. And then there had been the real surprise—watching the telegraph at work. And of course, something one could never forget: breakfast on the lawns of the Taj.

Delhi was like Lahore, with its bazaars, fort, the Juma Masjid, the Qutb, the river. I loved it, its crowded lanes and the way I could buy jewels in its bazaars. Fattehgarh seemed very far away when I was in Delhi. Then, after Meerut, there was the excitement of riding along the new Ganges canal near Roorkee with the smell of sugar cane all around us, mile after mile. Sometimes, as the news of our passing spread, the villagers would gather in groups, bowing low to me as I sat in the howdah or rode on my horse. There were no big crowds now, not like when I had gone to Fattehgarh from Lahore. But that had been two years earlier. I had then been a king recently deposed, a king going into exile, a young boy separated from his mother and his kingdom.

John Login, autumn 1893, Felixstowe

The man who walked into my tent in the parade ground of Roorkee was old and wizened. He wore a clean white dhoti and vest and his upper arms were covered with ink-blue tattoos. Bending low, he extended a rolled-up document tied with a red and gold thread. It was a letter from Mangla, the slave girl of Rani Jindan. She was nearby, she said, not far from Hardwar. She yearned to see the Maharaja. She had been with him and his mother since the day he was born. She had seen him open his eyes for the first time, take his first step, say his first word. For her he was a child, not a king. She begged to be allowed to see him once again. She would then be able to die in peace.

I had not forgotten Mangla. A clever and devious woman, if ever there was one. Even now she may be up to some trick, she may be intriguing with Jindan, I thought. I had in any case been reluctant to let Duleep tarry in Hardwar. The place would be teeming with pilgrims from the Punjab and they would surely recognize him. But if I had refused his wish to even go down to the Ganges, that tale too would have carried far and people would have attributed it to my determination to make him a Christian. But at meeting Mangla, I drew the line. I took a quick decision and conveyed it to her messenger there and then: 'Tell Mangla that no meeting with His Highness is possible. That is final.'

Duleep Singh, autumn 1893, Paris

A few of the irregular cavalry accompanied our elephant into Hardwar that morning. Login had sent off the rest of the escort, the riders, the sepoys, my carriage, on to Dehra so that people would think that I had actually left. He was always chary of displaying any sort of fanfare around me. For the same consideration, Dalhousie had already cut down my escort to a mere fifteen sentries. I learnt that he had laughed at Login's suggestion to take along several parties of irregular cavalrymen and infantrymen to set up my establishment in Mussoorie. I could not be at a greater risk than the Governor General of India himself, he said.

I had heard of Hardwar often, from Mangla and the other Hindu servants. They had always yearned to go and bathe in the holy waters of the Ganges. But it was a different thing to see it for myself, as the elephant lurched through the bazaars and went down towards the banks of the river. The pilgrims were everywhere, many with their heads shaven, eating puree aloo and drinking tall glasses of lassi. Every once in a while Shivdeo would tug at my arm as he heard the bells and conch shells from the temples. Finally we reached the steps that led down to the water. Under a thick clump of massive old trees, several holy men, their bodies smeared with ash, were performing penance. The mahout pointed out a man who stood on one leg, another who had been lying on a bed of nails for several months, yet another who had not come down from a tree for weeks.

Suddenly, there was a shout:

'Maharaj! Maharaj!'

I could see a hefty, bare-chested man, his wet dhoti clinging to his legs, pointing towards our elephant. Instantly, a number of people were heading towards us, their hands folded.

'Maharaj! Our king, our ruler!'

'The son of Ranjit Singh, long may he live.'

'May the gods smile on him, may he have a long and blessed life!'

The group gathered about the elephant, even as the mahout wheeled the animal around to head away from the ghat. I looked down at the crowd. I could see recognition, love, expectation. Just ordinary people of Punjab performing their teerath yatra, and they all remembered me, remembered Lahore.

Our elephant moved strongly up the slope of the ghat and the crowd followed. The riders came closer to the elephant, their spears guarding its rear, keeping the pilgrims at a safe distance. Soon we had left them behind. But a warm feeling stayed with me for a long time, along with a hope that I dared not speak out. Perhaps one of them would get word to my mother that I had been there, that I was well.

In the sky, the clouds had begun to growl, threatening to burst their grey-blue burden. When the elephant reached the spot where Login was waiting with the horses, fat drops of rain had begun to fall. 'We must ride fast, Your Highness, the elephants will follow. It is best to reach Dehra as soon as possible.'

The fierce rain chased us on the last leg of the journey to Dehra. In short bursts, we rode hard along the edge of the thick saal forest. The air was cool and fresh and pleasant and the rain had released all sorts of wild smells that intoxicated our senses. Once in a while we saw a cheetal or a buck crash through the thick undergrowth, startled by our approach. And during one of our halts we heard the blood-chilling roar of a tiger, not too far away. I could not remember when I had last enjoyed something more than this exhilarating ride through the rain.

We rode through the day, crossing empty stony riverbeds, up the gentle slopes of the early Siwalik hills and finally, down into the *doon* of Dehra. The undulating valley lay before us, its green beauty washed by the rain. Across it stood the Himalayan range, the highest mountains that I had ever seen, mauve in the evening light, their peaks catching the weak rays of the sun that had finally broken through the clouds. As we rode across the valley towards the foothills where we would camp on the road to Rajpur, Login pointed out the mountain ridge, above the strip of cloud, where the station of Mussoorie lay. My fascinated gaze followed Login's finger; that station would be home for the next few months.

John Login, autumn 1863, Felixstowe

I was enjoying my cup of tea on the veranda of my bungalow just below Duleep's castle that stood at the top of the hill. I had named the bungalow St Roque, after Lena's old house in England. It was pleasant, even in June, so different from Fattehgarh. As far as the eye could see, there were only comfortable shades of green. The castle was ringed with tall deodhars and pines and their sharp fragrance mingled with the sweetness of the champa flowers that Duleep had planted outside his bedroom. The valleys fell before me on three sides; behind me lay the higher slopes of Landour cantonment.

At the edge of the Castle Hill estate lay the civil station of Mussoorie and I could see the Mall winding its way to the other end of the station. In the morning it was a deserted strip, tired after the revelry that it provided to the residents of the station all evening. The early ray of the sun caught the steeple of the church.

There was no doubt that this estate had been the right choice. There were enough English companions for the Maharaja in the station and yet we were at a safe distance, secure as a fort. Not a person could approach him without the guards getting to know; and within the estate, Duleep was free to run and play, to ride through the tunnel that lay at one end of the estate, while his hawks scoured the hill for new types of insects and plants. In fact, I had even designed the gate to the estate like a gate of the Lahore fort. He could feel at home in this toy fort.

He was clearly enjoying the company of Shivdeo, Tommy Scott and the Boileau brothers, Frank and Charles. The last two were quite

a find, and that alone would have justified the move to Mussoorie.
Sons of Major Boileau in the cantonment, they had recently come
from home and showed all the signs of a careful and sophisticated
education. Their character, their diction and their deportment would
definitely impact on Duleep. If the boy had to get to like the English
and the Christian way of life, then there could be nothing better than
actual examples of his own age group. Like any other boy, he would
yearn to be like his playmates, to better them at all their pursuits. He
had already learnt, for instance, to eat like them. Since the journey
to Mussoorie had begun, Duleep had joined us at our table, along
with Tommy and Guise. He now ate freely of all the dishes that were
laid before him—there was no beef, of course. Every once in a while,
though, he did want his favourite Punjabi dishes. Things had moved
a long way since the day Duleep had insisted on having tea with
Tommy Scott. That one act had shown everyone, the servants,
Bhajan Lal, his English companions, the entire Sikh entourage, that
Duleep meant what he said. He was prepared to break caste, not
knowing that as a Sikh he really had no caste to break!

A volley of young, excited voices coming up the steep path
shook me from my reverie that June afternoon. The boys were
returning from their morning game of cricket from the ground that
we had cleared in a natural curve below the castle, facing the straight
slope of Landour. Duleep's enthusiasm for the game had infected the
other boys. Various attendants would be rounded up to field and
occasionally Guise and I would also join them. They would play in
the early mornings till about eight-thirty and then start again at
four-thirty in the evening. With all this cricket, hawking, archery
and riding, Duleep was looking less stout and his usually sallow
complexion shone with health.

The voices faded as the boys went into different parts of the
castle. To get ready for the lessons at ten sharp. Arithmetic, English,
geography, history and science with Guise and Urdu with the Munshi.
On Mondays and Thursdays Duleep would get two hours of tuition
in music and drawing from George Hunter, who taught in many of
the schools around the area and was truly a magnificent find. And
of course religious instruction continued all along. Duleep had to be
fully familiar with the scriptures if he was to live the life of a
practising Christian.

Duleep Singh, autumn 1893, Paris

I was fascinated by my companions. I wanted to be like Tommy,
like those two brothers who had just come from England, so
fresh that they still seemed to smell of the woods and the sea. I
loved the way they spoke, their polite, diffident manner, the way
they said sorry and thank you. I could dress like them, eat like them,
the same dishes—baked and grilled—and most of the time, I could
even speak like them. If there was a difference in accent, then I
didn't know it.

I had worked hard on all that, watched and learnt. It had seemed
the correct way of doing everything. I could do what each of them
did, man to man. I was better on a horse than all of them put
together and I could shoot as well as the next man. At our lessons,
I always scored better than most of them. And on the cricket field,
I got the ball across the boundary as often as the most English of my
companions.

I really had no choice, now that I think back on those days. I
had to be like them, as much like them as my brown skin and
native birth would allow. I had nothing to fall back upon—no
kingdom, no throne, no mother, no God. I have heard that there is
a wisdom in the blood, a life-knowledge, that is with us at all times
from our birth, and sometimes we are aware of things even when we
do not understand them. I was conscious of my condition, then,
even if I did not quite grasp it. And it was clear as day that I was
utterly alone and a nobody outside the world that Login and his
Lord Dalhousie had built for me. My pride, my station and all
comfort and excitement lay with them. The only way left was the
way forward, to England. Today, of course, I know how I was
misled, subtly. I was put into positions where I would want to do
what the Englishmen did, where all that mattered to me was the
approval of Login and Dalhousie.

When I saw all my companions dress up in their coats, white
shirts, ties and tophats and go to church every Sunday, leaving
Shivdeo with me, I felt lonely. It irritated me to be alone with him,
as if we were both the same, different from the others in some way.
It irritated me because unlike him, I had worked so hard at learning
the English way of life, had broken caste, cut off my long hair and

presented them to Lady Login, read the Bible every morning and night.

Every Saturday, I would send a message to Login, asking if I could go to church on Sunday. And each week there would be a polite denial conveyed through one of the servants.

Until finally one day, Login agreed.

John Login, autumn 1863, Felixstowe

It was the third week of September in Mussoorie and a pleasant sun warmed the entire station. On that Saturday when I received Duleep's usual request to accompany us to church on Sunday, I walked across to his rooms. There was an air of expectation amongst his attendants as they quietly watched me go into the Maharaja's chamber where he was sketching.

'Your Highness, I have got your message that you wish to accompany us to church tomorrow?'

'Yes, my dear friend, and are you going to say no again?'

'On the contrary. I had been waiting only for you to make sufficient advances in your English language lessons so that you could have the full benefit of the service. I think that has been achieved and for that, Your Highness, please allow me to commend you with all humility. Today, I had come to say that we would be pleased if you were to join us tomorrow.'

'Thank you,' replied Duleep Singh, unable to keep the excitement out of his voice.

'Your Highness, it is important that we do not make too much of this important occasion so as not to give cause for any unnecessary anguish to any party.'

Duleep had nodded. So far, everything related to his change of religion—the initial declaration, the religious education, the change in lifestyle—had been done with the minimum of fuss. This was an obsession with Lord D and I, sometimes against my own instincts, had gone along.

So the next day, quietly and soberly, Duleep walked down the slope from the estate and joined the congregation in the church. Bhajan Lal, dressed in his best, walked a few steps behind us. It was an important day for him too, a day of which he could be justifiably proud.

As it happened, Archdeacon Pratt was our guest for about ten days in Mussoorie during the autumn of 1852. He was highly regarded in the church hierarchy in India and had been a friend for many years. I used to enjoy our evening conversations on various matters. On one such evening I brought up the subject that was uppermost in my mind those days.

'You know, Duleep Singh has started going to church these days.'

Pratt's thin face was pinched in concentration.

'Yes, I have heard. And you are to be commended on the way all this has turned out.'

'I have done little. It is God's light that shines on him. He has been guided by the eternal hand.'

'Have you thought about his possible baptism?'

'I think about it all the time. But the situation has to be ripe. And of course, the Governor General and the Court of Directors would have to agree. I don't think that any step the Maharaja now takes will cause much excitement in this country. The natives are reconciled to the idea that he wants to be raised as a Christian. They know that he no longer observes Hindu rites and charities, that he much prefers the company of Europeans, that he eats at our table. In a way they have given up on him.'

Archdeacon Pratt nodded. 'You are right. Duleep Singh's case is now known all over British India and while once it had caused much excitement, it has now stopped being more than a passing curiosity. I also feel he has had a long enough training. If you like, I would be glad to talk to him to see how ready he is for the next step.'

'That would be awfully good of you. A testimonial from an Archdeacon would certainly help the case for baptism, as and when of course the Maharaja expresses such a desire and we approach Lord Dalhousie.'

Duleep, I think, was only too eager to please the Archdeacon. He had worked hard on his religious studies for more than a year and if the Archdeacon was there to test him, then I knew that the boy would treat it like any other test, the sort that Guise used to set for all the boys every week, in mathematics, history and science. And like Duleep scored high in those tests, he would want to do well here too.

Pratt was a clever man. As he told me later, he did not come to the subject at hand immediately. He first put the boy at ease by talking about the excellent bracing weather in Mussoorie, the various walks that he had been on in the area, the picnic spots that lay tucked away like gems, near waterfalls, caves and ancient temples. Duleep talked freely and comfortably and finally Pratt touched the crucial subject. He left me a full record of his meeting with Duleep.

'My congratulations, Your Highness, on the amazing progress you have made, as I understand from Dr Login, in all your studies, especially the study of the scriptures.'

'Thank you, I enjoy my lessons. But there is much to learn yet.'

I nodded.

'The service of God is a lifelong work. One is blessed to be a Christian in belief and in deed.'

'I am prepared. I would like to be like Dr Login, like Tommy and the others. Now I even go to Church on Sunday.'

'So I understand, Your Highness, and again, I commend you on what I have heard about your exemplary behaviour in Church. The solemnity and sincerity with which you have participated in service has impressed the entire station. And are you reading the Bible nowadays?'

'Of course. I read it daily, a chapter from the Old Testament in the morning and one from the New Testament in the evening before I go to sleep. Now of course I read it on my own. In the beginning, Bhajan Lal used to read it to me. My English was not too good then. He had to explain things to me. That is when I got interested in Christianity.'

'That was God's blessing. What were your feelings then, Your Highness, if you would excuse my curiosity?'

'When I heard the stories from the Bible then, when I heard of the crucifixion, of St Paul's conversion, it made me

feel like I was not living correctly. I felt that I was a sinner and only Christ could save me.'

I nodded approvingly. Duleep Singh continued speaking, encouraged by the approval.

'But I need to know more. It is only then, I hear, that I can get baptized.'

'I am sure, by God's grace, all things will happen in good time. But if you permit, Your Highness, we can now go through some of the matters that you must have already learnt.'

'Of course.'

'Tell me, Your Highness, what do you understand by the original sin?'

'Our first parents violated God's commandment and that resulted in their fallen nature—that is the original sin.'

'What is the difference between the original sin and the actual sins?'

'The sins that we commit are actual sins and they are born of the fallen nature that was created by the original sin.'

'What is the meaning of justification and what is sanctification?'

'Justification is our being forgiven freely by God and our being treated by Him as innocent. Sanctification is the worth of improvement, with God's blessings, in our hearts and lives.'

Pratt was pleased. As he left the room he told me that the Maharaja of Punjab was ready to receive baptism.

Back in Fattehgarh, Reverend Jay had replaced Reverend Carshore as the chaplain. In the early weeks of 1853, he confirmed, in writing, as per the desire of the Governor General, what Pratt had said to me in Mussoorie: the Maharaja was sufficiently familiar with the holy religion to receive the holy sacrament. What was more, on my gentle suggestion, Duleep had written to Lord Dalhousie that he wished to be baptized and had reiterated once again that he was doing it out of his own volition. He hoped that the God and Saviour whom he wished to make his own would enable him to live a Christian life. I also added my own conviction that the baptism was in perfect order and certified that Duleep, since his initial declaration, had shown truth, rectitude and consistency.

I knew Dalhousie would like that the ceremony be a quiet affair. We decided to hold it in Fattehgarh in the Maharaja's own house as the local church was undergoing repairs. And to make things simpler, the Maharaja had expressed a desire that he would like to be baptized in his own name. Finally, all the pieces were falling in place and I knew that when Dalhousie gave his go-ahead, he did it with a clean conscience.

Duleep Singh, autumn 1893, Paris

There are many bitter ironies of life. I wonder if any other Christian in all history has ever been baptized with water from the Ganges, holy to the Hindus! Not from any thought of softening the blow, or placating native feelings. Rather, Mrs Login thought that this act would add a holy dimension to the river for me, make it like the river Jordan, whose waters blessed Christ. So as I stood in my house in Fattehgarh among the local grandees, my faithful Jewindah ran down the lawn that sloped to the sandy bank of the Ganges and brought back water that had come from Badrinath and Hardwar and it was used to make me a Christian!

But forget the irony. From all I recall, I managed to go through the ceremony with the required dignity. It was shorn of any pomp and noise and I remember my heart welling up with the solemnity of the moment that I had prepared for so long. I was sure that all the traits that I had been taught were Christian—sincerity, commitment, honesty of character—showed in my face. After weeks of careful reading of the scriptures with the gentle Reverend Jay, I knew well the questions he would ask, the answers that I was to give, the vows that I had to take. How was I to know what I was doing? And in how many ways I would have to pay for it?

Now in this twilight, it is easy to know all the truths, easy to realize all the mistakes. If my people were considered duplicitous, then I have met scoundrels among Christians too and perhaps none greater than Dalhousie, who thought nothing of depriving me of all that was mine and then pretending to look after me as a father. All his concern for my well-being, his elaborate attempts to determine that nobody had influenced me in my choice of religion were sham, one big game of counterfeit. The truth was that politically, he wrote somewhere, he could have desired nothing better because the act of conversion destroyed my influence forever. He only hoped that my example would be multiplied in India, native princes one by one would hand over not only their kingdoms to the British but also their souls.

If there is a God, whatever kind of God, let him not put a trusting child in the hands of a scoundrel like that ever again . . .

Things were better during my second season in the hills. I felt a part of the family. I could go to church with all of them, stand in the sunlit square to gossip after the service, have lunch with everybody. I was no longer on test. I could concentrate on my music and art. I played the flute at many performances on the Mall. I sketched and painted in my room, at school and during picnics—birds and animals and waterfalls and cottages. And when people praised my art it made me happy.

My baptism seemed to open all doors. Dalhousie wrote to the Court of Directors in London that I should be sent to England for my own good. It would do me good to live among the English. It would fasten me forever to Christianity, make me industrious and save me from sinking into useless and degenerate indolence that other pensioned princes in India were famous for.

Anyway, there was nothing to hold me back. Dalhousie had made sure of that. Kingdom taken away, mother sent into exile, culture and religion switched. It was all very neat. And my tractable character, gentle disposition and pleasing ways would go a long way in making me the perfect example that could be followed by many in India. And I of course played right into Dalhousie's hands. I was happy to go to England. Happy to be allowed to eat and dress and speak like the English, to meet their Queen!

Ah, the innocence of a child!

Shivdeo wanted to go with me and Dalhousie had no reservations. Two birds with one stone, they must have thought. Let no one remain who can claim any influence in the Punjab. Let them all go and break caste by travelling across the seven seas. But when we reached Barrackpore his mother's wailing and screaming caught up with Shivdeo. She had written to Dalhousie threatening to commit suicide if her son was sent across the seven seas.

So, on the 19th of April 1854, I said goodbye to my Punjabi retainers on the deck of the steamer *SS Hindustan* that would take me to another world. Besides the Logins, there was also with me Nehemiah Goreh, a Brahmin who too had become a Christian. He would teach me oriental languages for three years.

As the ship steamed out of the harbour, I counted the twenty-one guns of the salute. I was sure that I would return soon after completing my education and would settle down as Login had planned, in a landed estate in Dehra, free to spend the summers in Mussoorie.

But in truth, that was the beginning of a long journey away from home, a journey that has not ended to this day.

Book Four

ELVEDEN

Duleep Singh, autumn 1893, Paris

I went into my exile innocently, almost joyously. Fascinated, I stood at the Great Pyramids at Giza and raced my companions to the top of the biggest one, climbing one massive ancient block after another, mindless of what had gone and what was to come. And then, as my ship passed Malta, and then Gibraltar, I counted anxiously the guns that boomed in salute. Still twenty-one. Still a Royal. Finally, my first sight of England, the true beginning of my exile . . .

Mrs Fagin.

That is what I once called Queen Victoria. The biggest pickpocket of them all. The receiver of stolen goods. Stolen kingdoms, stolen jewels.

Smuggled away to her by her loyal viceroys, men like Dalhousie, with immaculate records and long panegyrics. The thousands of pearls and emeralds and rubies and diamonds taken from my toshakhana and presented to her by the East India Company after the Great Exhibition of 1851. To be locked away in the Tower of London, stuck in her tiara, sewn on her dresses.

That's how she received the Koh-i-noor. Dalhousie tucked it away into a chamois bag especially made by his wife, which was then sewn into his belt by Login.

Today it matters little to me whether I have it or not. If I had it who knows what I might do with it. Perhaps I would trade it for a few sunny days, a few happy conversations, some justice, a fair enquiry into my case, and certainly for a journey to Punjab. Or just throw it into the river for all that it has done for me. But as a child, I used to yearn for it. Especially when the courtiers would set up durbar in Fattehgarh and talk of the lost glory of Lahore.

I did see the near-mythical stone once in my years of exile; I even held it in my hand for a few moments. It happened on an evening in Buckingham Palace, soon after my arrival in England. The Queen was very fond of me those days and I must admit so was I, of her and her family. She was having my portrait painted by that artist Winterhalter. The man did a good job. He made me look tall and handsome, like a real prince. He was used to painting European royalty and I suppose he knew how to massage egos, even the ego of a Maharaja without a throne. He said I would 'grow into the picture'. I never was to grow that tall but I hope people will remember me like he made me look, and not how I actually have become, bald and fat.

He would make me pose two hours at a time in the White Drawing Room of the palace. The Queen would come in just to watch me, every inch her loyal subject, with her portrait set in diamonds around my neck and her miniature picture in a ring on my finger.

Yes, she had reason to be fond of me those days. I was such a great addition to her banquets; a fine specimen to show off to the rest of society. A young oriental king who spoke English and, to top it all, was Christian. I also said things that must have eased her conscience. I would tell her that I was glad to be in England, far away from the violent ways of my people. I even told her, on a ferry ride to the Isle of Wight, that I had become a Christian because of my own beliefs, that I had broken caste by having tea with Tommy Scott and by drinking from the same glass as Lady Login in front of Rani Dukhno. I exculpated everybody—Dalhousie, Login, Lady Login, even Bhajan Lal from having anything to do with my change of faith and took it all upon myself.

Is one still a child at sixteen, to be forgiven such complete surrender to manipulation . . .?

But I was talking of the Koh-i-noor and the days of the Winterhalter portrait.

One of those mornings, Lady Login and I were riding in Richmond Park when she turned towards me suddenly.

'Maharaja, have you ever thought of seeing the Koh-i-noor again?'

A prickly excitement ran through me. For a moment, I thought that everything was turning out all right. The coming to England, becoming a good Christian and everything else had been worth it, that I was being rewarded for my good behaviour. Maybe not just the diamond but all else that it implied would be given back to me. But I kept the excitement out of my voice as I wheeled my horse back at the far end of the park.

'Yes, Lady Login, I would very much like to see the Koh-i-noor again,' was all I said.

I was still not prepared for what happened a few evenings after that conversation. I was standing very still for Winterhalter. All of a sudden the curtains parted and four tall beefeaters in full dress down to their sabres entered the room. An official stood timidly between them, holding a large box. From the corner of my eye, I saw Her Majesty walk quickly to the official and open the box. She held it and for a moment both she and the Prince Consort stared quietly at whatever it was inside the box. Then she called me.

'Maharaja! I have something to show you.'

I stepped off the dais and walked quickly to her.

She held out the open box towards me.

'The Koh-i-noor, Maharaja. I understand that you had wanted to see it.'

I looked again at the magical diamond that had been mine, that had meant so much to me, my father, my beautiful, fiery mother, my people. It seemed much smaller than I remembered it.

'I have had it cut, Maharaja, by the best cutters available. It shines better now.'

She picked it out of the box and put it in my palm. I took it between my thumb and forefinger and held it up to the light. I could not look away from the quiet dazzle. I stood staring at it near the open window and a rush of emotions began to drown me. I realized I had lost everything, I was no longer a king. I was only being made to dress up like one and amuse the Queen's court. I was angry, angry enough to want to fling the diamond in the lawns below. I was sad. I was demeaned. What did Her Majesty want me to do? To kneel down and thank her for showing me what in fact belonged to me?

When the rush in my blood subsided I knew what I wanted to do. I would make it clear that the Koh-i-noor was mine by right. So far, it had been stolen from me. Now I would gift it to her.

I walked back from the window to Her Majesty.

Handing the box with the diamond back to her I said: 'It is to me, Ma'am, the greatest pleasure thus to have the opportunity of myself tendering to my Sovereign the Koh-i-noor.'

I do not think she understood how I had felt. I do not think she cared enough. For her it was only a passing whim, a show of preposterous royal magnanimity, or a fitting show of loyalty.

But how does it matter now, all this business of so long ago?

John Login, autumn 1863, Felixstowe

Duleep was in England, certainly, but my task was far from over. I continued my labours, as did my good wife, as we were certain that the Lord wished us to carry on as guardians to Duleep. He was sixteen when he left India, grown up in his own country but still a child in ours. He could speak English but he needed more than that to make a life in England.

It was God's grace that Her Majesty accepted him with so much love. We felt that in some ways it was recognition of our efforts. And when, in all her graciousness, Her Majesty decided to confer the knighthood on me, I felt truly humbled by the Lord's kindnesses. The Prince Consort and the royal children all were genuinely fond of Duleep and so was he of them. The young princesses once had great joy in cooking a repast of boiled potatoes with his assistance! With the friendly assistance of the Prince Consort, Duleep even learnt to take photographs and took some memorable ones of the royal family. And Her Majesty never forgot his birthday. The royal gift would always arrive on time—a thoroughbred hunter, a dog, an excellent timepiece and many others.

Duleep Singh, autumn 1893, Paris

Login was all right, I suppose, as was Colonel Oliphant who was later appointed as my equerry. In fact, Login and his wife had almost been like my parents. My own mother I could only yearn for in secret, ever since I had been separated from her. I would sit for hours thinking whether I would ever be able to meet her. She too must have yearned for her Dula ji, to see me as a young man, perhaps not on the throne of Lahore but as one who could dine with Queen Victoria. But I only knew that she was alive, and in exile in Nepal. I did what I could under the circumstances. When Nehemiah Goreh went back to India, I gave him a letter for her and told him to deliver it to her personally in Nepal. But he was not allowed to reach Nepal and passed on my message to her through a travelling ascetic.

And so I continued, finding what warmth I could in the care of the Logins. But Login's guardianship had continued too long; it was like a noose around my neck. I should have been allowed to manage my own affairs when I became sixteen, as was customary in India. I wanted to go where I wanted, spend what I felt like. Even the Lahore treaty had not made me a prisoner. But Dalhousie decided that I could not be treated of age until I was eighteen. And then they wanted me to wait till I was twenty-one, treating me like an Englishman in this one matter!

I now know that it was all about money. They were reluctant to give me proper accounts—about how much had been paid to me and how much was due under the Terms of Annexation. The only time that they did supply me a figure—1861, I think—nearly a hundred thousand pounds remained in my favour.

Measly merchants, that was what the East India Company was made up of, petty accountants behaving like emperors.

John Login, autumn 1863, Felixstowe

Duleep was still young when he began to raise issues about his affairs. He was young but began to show an intelligence and canniness that we may not have thought him capable of some years ago. He would discuss the Terms of Annexation with me many times and often I would be surprised by the deep thought that he had given to matters despite his natural inclination to spend his days in indolence. Perhaps, ironically, it was all the education that he had received that had now equipped him to question his destiny.

He was uneasy that he was not his own master, not at sixteen, not even at eighteen. It worried him that he could not decide where he could reside. But his biggest problem lay—and it still does—with articles four and five of the Terms that deal with his pension. He is to receive a pension, for himself, his relatives and servants of the state: a sum not less than four lakh rupees and not more than five lakh. He believes that this is all allotted to him, not to each of the relatives and servants separately. Hence any lapsed payments due to deaths and so on should devolve on him, if not personally, then at least into a fund for his benefit. He has wanted, for long, to go back to India and buy an estate for himself with those lapsed funds. And he believes that the pension is hereditary and will pass on to his eventual children. Dalhousie and all others have argued the opposite. He is entitled to only a part of the pension personally and that is to stop with his death. He has no right, they believe, on the lapsed pensions. And thereby hangs a tale.

Duleep Singh, autumn 1893, Paris

I have read the Terms of Annexation so many times in Aithison's Treaties that they are emblazoned on my heart. These were Terms that were supposed to give a veneer of decency to Dalhousie's 'conquest' of Punjab, a 'conquest' whose cause lay in his own army not acting in time, and the blame falling on my head, his ward, all of nine or ten. But what cared he for me; he only pretended to be solicitous. He gifted me a Bible before I sailed for England in which he wrote: '. . . *this holy book in which he has been led by God's grace to find an inheritance richer by far than all earthly kingdoms is presented with sincere respect and regard by his faithful friend . . .*'

Having deprived me of my inheritance, he *hoped* that I may acquire another which was not in his power to bestow. What he actually thought about me, I discovered when I read his letter to his friend Hobhouse. He called me 'a child notoriously surreptitious, a brat begotten of a bhisti, and no more a son of Ranjit Singh than Queen Victoria is'. That was what he really thought of me, the rest was deception and fraud.

Only the Queen was gracious. She wrote to Dalhousie that I should be treated fairly. And what have I ever asked for? Only that which was promised by treaty and that too was peanuts compared to what they would end up paying even their enemies. Wajid Ali Shah of Oudh, whom they always called a drunken debauchee, was paid fifteen lakh every year and another three for his guards and more for his relatives. And Oudh had broken every pledge that it had made to the British Empire, unlike my father who for decades had remained a friend of the British.

So I wrote to the Court of Directors of the East India Company. I left it to them to make me a fair and liberal settlement, and young as I was, I put it all in good faith and left for Italy. By that time I had already picked up a smattering of Italian, besides some German, and was quite eager to try them out . . .

Ah Europe of my youth! Some pleasant memories there—of my friend Ronald Leslie-Melville, who did not need much persuasion to accompany me, along with the Logins of course. Marseilles. The blue Mediterranean. Nice . . . Florence . . . Rome . . . Venice . . . Geneva. Memories of many adventures, pleasant evenings with friends, new and enchanting sights and some awful memories of a miserable cold that I caught in Venice, where both Ronald and I were laid up, the poor fellow for much longer than I. And when I came back, there was still no answer from the Company about a final settlement for me and all hopes of going back to India too were dashed, since the Mutiny had broken out.

A word about the Mutiny before I die, about the ones I left behind in India. Both my tutor, Walter Guise, and Elliot, my loyal steward, tried to escape from Fattehgarh down the Ganges in boats. But they did not get far. The mutineers captured them and massacred them on the parade ground of Cawnpore.

My Fattehgarh estate was plundered and reduced to ruins. Login tried to launch a search for the valuables that had been put into the Collector's treasury or left in the residence, but nothing was ever found again, all sold and disposed of.

The Governor General's agent who answered Login's queries put the blame on a notorious rebel of the area with a huge ransom on his head. I lost again, even though my Sikhs remained loyal to the British through the Mutiny, despite what had been done to their kingdom.

Immediately after the Mutiny, I was informed of the decision that I could manage my own affairs. So I celebrated with a shooting trip in Sardinia. The thought of Sardinia brings up one solitary

happy memory of a young beauty who took full charge of my heart
for a while. Strange how one can remember places, times, the
seasons, just by the thought of a pretty face. But today, try as I
might, I cannot recall her name. I used to lose my heart easily those
days—or was it that I was so desperate for love? Several young ladies,
in quick succession, appeared to me as the perfect answer to my
quest for a bride, much to the consternation of those around me,
particularly Lady Login and even Her Majesty.

Is it that a man robbed of his will and his identity becomes so
prone to seductions that he becomes a plaything for whoever is the
God of the senses and the emotions? And how just and loving was
I to those who gave me their love? Did I make them only the objects
of my amusement?

John Login, autumn 1863, Felixstowe

Even in 1859, Duleep's patience with Her Majesty's government was
at a stretch.

'Do, for goodness' sake,' he wrote to me, 'get the government to
settle with me, and pay my arrears as soon as possible! I do believe
they will take another year to settle my affairs . . .'

I have pushed his case persistently as I have wanted our people
to do what is liberal and right towards the Maharaja so that I can
hold up my head in front of him. He has trusted me to fight his
battles, even when he has come of age. He has set an excellent
example to his peers by his loyalty and goodwill. And he has been
kind to me. Half my salary all these years has come from his
resources and even now he has settled an annuity on me, which the
Company would only let me accept after I had tendered my
resignation. They forgot that I had laboured for a larger cause than
my own comfort, that I had given up a medical career. The way they
have treated me, I can better understand Duleep's frustrations.

We should have settled when the going was easy. Before it had
become complicated with his demands about compensation for his
Fattehgarh property and before Rani Jindan had filled his mind with
tales about his private properties.

Duleep Singh, autumn 1893, Paris

I can now see my own naivety. I had genuine hopes for a fair settlement. Fairness and justice! I was always told that these were the essential qualities of the English. I should have known better, after having my kingdom illegally annexed. And naively I hoped that by good behaviour I would also be able to get to Bibiji, once again be together with her somewhere. At the same time I fell for all their subtle offers, including the inducement of a quiet life in England.

Those were the days of living in Castle Menzies in Scotland, walking the moors in a kilt, hawking and shooting to my heart's content, attending daily entertainments and picnics. It was the time too when everybody wanted me to marry Princess Gowramma, the daughter of the Raja of Coorg. The Logins, and even Her Majesty, found so many similarities as to make them believe that there could be no better match for either of us. After all, my kingdom had been taken away as had been her father's. He was a political prisoner in India for many years, as my mother had been, and then he was in England, like I was.

She too had been baptized as a Christian—in the very presence of her Hindu father. And, like me, she enjoyed Her Majesty's favours; in fact she was the Queen's god-daughter. Brought up, even before me, as a European. Taught how to dress and eat, and not to be bothered with caste. Everybody would have been delighted, all consciences would have been salved.

Only I wasn't enthused, and I sometimes wonder why. She had it all, in a way—she was nice looking, fair as a European, of royal descent and a Christian. But I was buying none of it. I liked Gowramma but could not think of her as a wife. Besides, my youthful fancy had fixed itself on someone else.

Lady Lena Login, winter 1893, Felixstowe

I must confess that I had hoped that the Maharaja would take Gowramma for his wife. The Lord seemed to have prepared her well to be his partner. She came of royal blood and like him, had seen the true faith when just a child. True, her native influences had not left her totally and she got into a scandalous escapade with a stable boy when she was under the guardianship of Mrs Drummond. There too I saw the hand of the Lord. Her Majesty decided that I should take care of her and though my hands were full, I agreed, thinking that it would bring her and Duleep under the same roof, so to speak. It would strengthen the bonds that must surely have been there because of their similar situations and time spent together at Kew and Castle Menzies.

But Duleep's reluctance to turn their friendship into anything stronger soon became obvious, though I did not really accept it until the time we met up in Rome. He had been shooting in Central Europe with a much older companion, the dashing Samuel Baker. But the trip had obviously not gone as well as planned.

'It was too cold on the Danube,' he told me, as he sat alone with me one evening. 'The big steamers were not plying because of the ice. But we tried to go on in a sort of passenger boat. That too sprung a leak and we decided to move on by land through Wallachia and Bucharest. Some very fine shooting there—partridge, geese, duck, even bustard. But I couldn't realize my secret ambition of getting a wild boar. Finally, though Baker seemed fine enough, the cold got to me. I wanted to get away. So I went on alone to Constantinople. What a city, Lady Login, and how blue is the Bosphorus! The warmth did me good, else I would not have been able to join you at all.'

'I'm glad you are here, Maharaja. Sir John and I are always so happy to have you with us. And I am sure Gowramma will be delighted,' I said.

He was lost in thought for a while.

'I think I need to talk to you about the Princess,' he said after a few moments.

I waited in silence as he carried on.

'I know the Princess has gained greatly from being with you. She is vastly improved in every way, but please understand my sentiments. I do not think that she is suited for marriage with me.'

I could not keep the agitation out of my voice.

'But why, Maharaja? She is so pretty, so accomplished and now she has all the graces. And she is like us, devoted to God and Christian values.'

'I know what you are thinking. That she is suited in so many ways for someone in my position. Otherwise whom will I marry? Some heathen Indian who will be forced to become a Christian only to please me? Or some European with whom I will produce half-castes? But that besides, I cannot marry her. She will not be able to make me happy. I could never feel more than pity for her. I don't have the confidence in her; I cannot seem to trust her. I would hate to have trouble after marriage.'

'But Maharaja, she will make you happy.'

'Nothing can make me happy, Lady Login. That is how I think sometimes. No, often. I am lonely, I am desolate, I am dead inside. I succumb to every passing temptation. I am always living on the edge of destruction. I need to be strong, Lady Login, I need to live the life of a good Christian as you have taught me. Presently there are no ties that hold me, no bonds, no family. There is no hope, there is no reward that I can work towards and urge myself to behave better to attain it.'

'Maharaja, I have never heard you speak like this. What is the matter?'

I was not at all prepared for what was to follow. He took my hand in his and speaking ever so softly, almost in a whisper, told me that he was deeply in love with ——, one of our young relatives from my husband's side. I do not now want to name her; it will serve no purpose whatsoever. I made him promise, too, and he never mentioned her to anyone . . . But that day, his emotions overcame him and tears began to flow down his cheeks as he looked at me pleadingly.

I must confess that I was at a total loss for words.

'I think you should go and calm down, Maharaja. We will talk about all this tomorrow,' was all I managed.

But the next day was no better. Duleep looked like he hadn't slept much as he addressed my husband and me in a state of high agitation.

'*You* know, better that anyone else, how difficult it is for me to get to know someone so well as I have come to know——. I know her sweet and amiable nature, her temper and her emotions. I worship her feelings towards God. I know that she is truthful and honest and she has every virtue in her that I would like in a wife. And I know all this since I have had the good fortune of living in the same family as her, and with no other family could I ever feel the same. And yet somehow I know that even *you* are going to reject the idea. Even you, for so many years the only parents I have known, are not really going to accept me as your own. You took me away from what I have known earlier, my country, my people, even my faith. I lost all chance of ever being one with my own race and if I still cannot be treated as one of your own, then I do not know where to turn to.'

John and I had talked over the matter at night and I listened as he gently spoke to Duleep.

'We understand your feelings, Maharaja. Please do not think that we are answering them with rejection—that would not be a very Christian thing to do. But we do think you need to give these feelings time to grow. If in the fullness of time your feelings are still the same, and if your progress in our way of life continues the way it has, then perhaps you could be permitted to plead your own case to ——.'

Reluctantly, the Maharaja accepted our decision. I was finally convinced that he would never marry Gowramma; perhaps her somewhat free ways had given him the wrong impression. I tried to find her a spouse among the Prussian nobles but there too she had little success. It was then that I decided that I would hand over her charge, and mercifully, Her Majesty agreed. Little did I know that Gowramma had not quite gone out of my life.

Duleep Singh, autumn 1893, Paris

I nursed my love for her through the seasons—all these years later I will still not commit her name to paper; I had given Lady Login my word, and at least in this I will be a king—I will honour my word. I wrote her many letters expressing my emotions but Lady Login returned those letters to me, unopened. But it was only when I managed to ask the dear girl herself that I accepted the inevitable. We were not fated to get married.

But it was left to me finally to get Gowramma married off. And what delicious irony there was in that. I introduced her to Lady Login's elder brother, Colonel John Campbell, and shortly the two were married, without the Logins even knowing about it! The Colonel was older to the Princess by about thirty years but he was a dashing man. They paid me a visit at Auchlyne, where there was good shooting that year. I remember getting ninety-three brace of my own gun one of those days. The Logins were also up there, but they left as soon as they knew that Campbell and Gowramma were coming up. They were still angry that they had known nothing of this match that I had made!

But the poor Princess did not live long. Within three years she had been buried in Brompton cemetery, killed by consumption. She left behind my god-daughter, a child called Edith Victoria Gowramma. That was a sad time, a time of death and desolation. Fate would deal me several quick blows and take away Gowramma and my mother and John Login, as well as my old valet Thornton and my secretary Cawood. All in a trice, leaving me alone . . .

Through those years, in the secret recesses of my heart, I yearned for the touch of Bibiji's hands, hands gone now forever, preserved only in the marble cast that lies at Elveden. She had beautiful hands, my mother, the thin blue veins shining faintly through the lovely transparent skin.

I could not get to her in Nepal. Our messengers were caught, our missives intercepted. Even from far she kept alive the struggle, sending support and encouragement to the Sikh warriors who fought against the annexation. She was the mystic beacon for all Sikhs, a figure of martyrdom and courage, one who had been ill-treated, whose son had been taken away . . . For fourteen years I was kept away from my mother. Lord Rama too went into exile for fourteen years, but a stepmother had cursed him. What was the curse that I was under?

Finally one of my letters, written after the Mutiny, reached her by a roundabout route. From Login to the British Resident in Nepal and then to my mother through a minister of the Nepal court. I had written that now that the country was quiet again, I hoped to get the government's permission to go back to India to see her. And such

was the changed thinking after the Mutiny, that I was even allowed
a reply.

She was overjoyed. *Dula ji*, she replied—the only person in the
whole wide world who called me thus—*your letter is like the nectar
of life to a dead person, my heart has expanded like a new-bloom rose,
my eyes that have been sick for years are cured at the sight of your
letter . . .*

I have her letter still in my papers in Elveden; it was the first that
I had ever received from her after growing up. I suddenly felt that
there was someone, after all, to whom I belonged, whose blood
flowed in my veins, whose every thought I could anticipate and
understand even before she had uttered it. I felt again a child.

She was my mother; that was what mattered to me. It still
matters to me, especially on days such as these, when the light begins
to fail very fast, and I feel that if my eyes close they will never again
open to another dawn.

It does not matter to me what the British thought of her, the
slanderous stories that they invented about her and the lies they
wrote down in their files and history books: that she was only a
minor queen of an ageing king, little more than a concubine. That
she was the Messalina of Punjab. That she took on many lovers—
Suchet Singh, Lal Singh and so many others. That I was the son not
of the Lion of Punjab, but perhaps of a bhisti who used to walk
around the gardens of Lahore fort, into the royal rooms and the
harem with a leatherskin full of water on his back . . .

Determined though I was—and acutely anxious about my
mother's welfare—it wasn't easy to get permission to go back to
meet her. The proposal was not received well in any quarter; even
Her Majesty was not keen. They thought that once I got together
with my mother I would make trouble for them. The truth is that
when they brought me away in 1854, they had meant it to be for
good. But they had not bargained with my desire to see my mother
again, to make some sort of arrangement that would take care of her
and not let her languish during her last years in exile in Nepal.

I wanted to go back for other reasons too. I had to see whether
I would be allowed at all, and how I would feel when I went back.
I had seen so much, learnt so much . . . And forgotten so much. I

had lost my home and my kingdom and my court had long been scattered; but I had been a grandee at Victoria's court. Was it that I only imagined a yearning for home? Perhaps I would discover that home was England, and nowhere else.

Ultimately, they agreed. Sir Charles Wood at the India Office replied that I could visit any part of India east of the Jumna, beyond which I would need the permission of the Governor General. Always a prisoner, always on a leash. But this can only be till my death. Beyond that even the British Empire cannot reach.

The question followed me on the steamer when I finally sailed home early in 1861. Someone asked me whether I intended to go back to Punjab.

'The British government does not trust me,' I replied bluntly.

My words got to Lord Canning, who, incidentally, tried to do all the right things. He sent his ADC to receive me on board the ship as it docked in Calcutta, and to escort me to the Spence Hotel. He ordered a twenty-one-gun salute and organized several receptions and dinners at Government House.

But he could not resist asking me what I had meant by the remark.

'Well, if you do trust me, then why not let me go where I like?' I asked him in return.

'It is not that we do not trust you,' he replied. 'But we do not want to have to punish or restrain people whose sentiments may be aroused on seeing you.'

I let that pass, for how does one respond to the insult of being expected to take such stupidity seriously? But their not letting me go to Punjab could not stop the Sikhs from coming to me. A regiment of Sikh soldiers on their way back from China heard that I was at the Spence Hotel. They would come and sit below my window and would not go away until I came out on the balcony.

'Sat Sri Akal!' they would shout.

And with folded hands I would return their greeting. They were my people, and they had not forgotten me.

But it is the pain and joy of those Calcutta evenings with Bibiji that I remember best. Only then did I realize how much I had missed her. To see her looking old and weak, though she was not much over forty, saddened and angered me.

'How have they treated you, Bibiji?' I would ask. 'What have you been through while I have been far away?'

'It is all in the past, my torture and deprivation. Today, my world is bright. Waheguru has given me a chance, even with the dying light of these eyes, to see my handsome son again.'

Evening after evening, the lost years began to come alive.

One day she would recollect the last days of Lahore ... 'I don't know who was wrong or who right. Perhaps the fault lay with us, we were rotten inside. Too many greedy men, hungry for honours and jagirs. Else we would have been able to keep the English out of Punjab. Perhaps I was short-sighted. I fed too many snakes.'

She would then recount how Ranjit Singh's mighty empire had crumbled in a matter of ten years. How deception, intrigue, treachery had led us into the waiting, avaricious hands of Dalhousie.

On other days, she would be in stronger spirits and tell me of how she had never given up the fight.

'They thought they would break me by locking me up—in Summan, then in Sheikhupura prison, then in Chunar fort. But they don't know Jindan! They took everything away, my jewels, my servants ... never was royalty treated this way. But I managed always to know what was happening in Punjab. I got my messages out. We had plans that would have caused rebellion in many British paltans. My loyal men were all over Punjab. Many of them, brave men, have been killed, their relatives tortured. Even the gardeners in the prison who sent me flowers were tortured. Then I threw dust in their eyes and escaped from Chunar fort.'

I begged her to tell me how she had managed that.

'I went away disguised as my own seamstress. And I even left a letter for the firanghi. I got out by my magic, I told them, and not as a thief—I woke up the Angrez guard as I left! They had pushed Jindan too hard. She had to show them what she could do.'

One of her Punjabi servants had taken her by boat on the Gomti and finally she had reached Patna.

'I stayed a while there, praying at the gurudwara. What better place in which to ask for courage than in the gurudwara that marks the birthplace of the tenth Guru? And then for many weeks I travelled through the forests and mountains as a bairagan, eating what people gave me in charity, sleeping where I could, until I reached Nepal. There I sent a message to the Rana. He gave me asylum, a house on the banks of the river in Kathmandu. But the Angrez sahib there would not meet me. I wanted to know where you were, whether my child was well and cared for. Finally they sent me news that they were taking care of you and were giving you a pension. But my eyes have yearned every day for a sight of your face, my child.'

And some days she would ask me to tell her what had happened to me since the day they took me away to Shalimar Bagh and her away to Sheikhupura jail. I told her of my Fattehgarh days, of learning English, of reading the Bible ... Bibiji held me close and cried when I told her of my baptism. And she listened, curious and fascinated, as I told her of my long journey to England, my visits to Buckingham Palace and the banquets given by Her Majesty. I even told her how I had held the Koh-i-noor in my hands again.

'Do you like it there, my child?' she asked me one evening.

'I have no choice, Bibiji. They will not let me return to Punjab. This time too they have let me come back this far only because they want to be seen as reasonable people—of course they've assured themselves that I will be no trouble. They have allowed me here so that I can make some arrangement for you—take you with me or settle you in Delhi, Bombay, even Mussoorie. But I have had enough of this separation. I want us to be together forever. I want to stay here with you.'

'I had thought, my child, that I would see you once and then spend the rest of my days somewhere on the banks of the Ganga in the contemplation of God. But now my decision is clear. We will remain together, wherever they permit us.' Something in my mother's voice seemed to suggest that my coming to her had resolved something—as if there was a life she had that she was giving up just to be with me, her son, and the feeling made me happy, happier than at any other time in my life.

On those days, when I stood on the balcony of my rooms at the Spence Hotel, I did not want to leave India. The fresh green plain that led to the river, with the fort on its banks, the banyan trees, the tamarind trees and faraway, the coconut trees, swaying in the warm breeze. There were smells that I had forgotten, colours that I had not seen for many years in England. Even though I had left when I was little more than a child, clutching in my hands the Bible that Lord Dalhousie had presented me, somewhere in my mind these smells and colours still lived. On other days I did not feel well at all. I felt chained in, unable to go where I wanted, tired of the persistent questions about my life from my old servants. I made plans and threw them out of the window one after the other. Take my mother and go back for a life of comfort in England, or find a way to stay back with her and possibly always be on the run?

Finally the decision was taken out of my hands. Bibiji had to leave India, only then would her jewels be restored to her. So I had to leave India once again.

John Login, autumn 1863, Felixstowe

It fell to me to help Rani Jindan clear all her jewels without payment of customs duty when she arrived in England early in the summer of 1861. So eager had been the government in India to see her depart for England, thus taking with her forever the possibility of fomenting trouble in the Punjab, that they agreed to return her all the jewels. For good measure, they threw in a pension of three thousand pounds a year. The jewellery was quite a collection, more than five hundred items—pearl necklaces, gold headbands and armlets, diamonds and ruby drops, and so much more—all neatly tabulated by Captain Rennie, the officer nominated to collect them from the treasury and dispatch them in twenty-one boxes on the steamship *Simla*.

When Duleep had gone to India to meet her, it had seemed hardly likely that she should accompany him back. But once mother and son got together, plans had obviously changed. Duleep wrote that he was not sure he was coming back to England, though at times he found India beastly and abhorred the attitudes of the natives. I think he had got unused to the sly and flattering oriental ways that must have inevitably greeted him. I tempted him with descriptions of a sporting estate that I had spotted for him in Scotland, a heaven of a place called Applecross with a deer forest to boot—hunting was his great passion. I knew that he yearned to be back. But his mother's power over him was not to be scoffed at. And she had always been a clever one. Once she declared that she would not be separated from her son again, come what may, there was no other alternative but for them both to come away to England.

Besides clearing her jewels through customs, I also found appropriate lodgings near our own in Lancaster Gate. And it was only natural that after her arrival, we began to see a lot of her. Years in exile and ill health had taken their toll on her. She was still beautiful, but not as before; she had aged fast, and her sight was almost gone. The years of flight and exile had taken their toll. But every once in a while, her spirit showed its flash.

'Thank you very much, Login sahib,' she said to me one day. 'Had I known then that you would be such a kind and helpful man and would prove to be so useful, I would not have tried to poison you in Lahore.'

Clearly, her informers had created a very different picture of me than the person she had finally met. I told her politely that I had all along been aware of her little project, as a whisper had reached my ears. Which only made the Rani laugh!

Lena, showing her usual solicitude, called on the Rani, though she was quite taken aback by the sights and smells of that very oriental household, complete with servants cooking Indian curries in the basement. Lena had never met the Rani before but she had heard tales of her beauty and love of intrigue. Naturally she was disappointed to meet the Rani in her present half-blind state. A few days later, the Rani paid a return visit to our house. For the occasion she wore a European dress, complete with her huge crinoline over her Indian costume and so unwieldy was she that two servants had to pick her up the stairs and then on to the settee.

It was easy to be charmed by her unconventional, dramatic ways. But as I had feared, her influence over Duleep was undiminished. The understanding had been that she would stay separately; if constantly together, she could fill his mind with all sorts of things, exactly the reason that she had been separated from him in the first place. But he clearly did not want to leave her and insisted on taking her with him to Mulgrave in the autumn of 1861. He even wrote to Lena asking for advice about getting a good likeness of hers done in oils.

'Let your mother stay at the neighbouring estate of Lythe Hall,' I wrote to Duleep. 'In that manner she will be near you and yet you would be able to have the independence that you are used to.'

'I am afraid that arrangement is not good for her, or for me,' he responded. 'We both feel that we have lost too much time in separation and whatever is still given to us by God should be spent together.'

This constant companionship could only lead to trouble. Duleep's moral character was bound to erode. My fears were soon proved true.

'I very much wish to have a conversation with you about my private property in Punjab and the Koh-i-noor diamond . . .' Duleep wrote to me just before he left Mulgrave that year. I had never heard him refer to private properties before and it was only his mother who could have told him about all that. She was being the evil genius of her son and turning his mind in many other ways too, as he struggled between being her loyal and loving son and becoming an English squire. One day he would tell me of his dreams of chasing foxes and shooting partridge in the country and another day he would want to take whatever the India Office gave him and go and set up an estate in India or open a Christian school for Punjabis. I was afraid that if he remained under her influence too long, much of our good work would be undone.

Duleep Singh, autumn 1893, Paris

It was in those days with Bibiji that I began to learn about what had really happened, about the extent and enormity of my loss, my private estates that had been taken away as if they were State property.

'Your father, his father and grandfather were possessed of large landed estates—houses, villages, agricultural lands, salt mines,' Bibiji told me again and again. 'Gujranwala, Wazirabad, Chakowal, Ram

Nagar ... all these belonged to your father even before he became monarch of Lahore. All these are yours after the death of Kanwar Naunihal Singh. These are private properties, they cannot be taken away under any treaty.'

I read the Terms closely again. It was true. Only State property was being 'confiscated', not my private estates. Confiscated! I had not been their vassal nor a defeated enemy but their ward, by treaty. Yet, not a penny have I got out of my private properties. They haven't even told me what all there is; in fact, they even deny that any such exists. My solicitors sent an agent to examine the land records of the Punjab. They noted that sixty-one villages in Gujranwala, another ten in Gujerat, yet another fifty-five in Jhelum and eighteen in Sialkot belonged to me personally. Also, the salt mines of Pind Dadur Khan and God knows what else. The revenue of the salt mines alone is now almost four hundred and fifty thousand pounds.

And the India Office had the temerity to offer me just three thousand pounds as compensation for what I lost in the pillage of Fattehgarh during the 1857 Mutiny! An insult, that is what it was, when I had lost land and houses, tents and equipment, carpets, elephant saddles ... Insults one remembers, no matter how much time passes. The Fattehgarh estate was set up at my expense. I had to pay for the trappings of my exile. They sold the houses and the grounds and refused to account for them. Now they have even lost interest while for me it becomes more crucial by the day.

'All the jewels were inherited,' Bibiji explained. 'They belonged to the family. All private property. Have they told you what they did with the jewels?'

The Koh-i-noor diamond, I know, was to be 'surrendered' to Queen Victoria. 'Surrendered', not 'confiscated'. Therefore it was seen to be my private property. If even Dalhousie could see that I had private property, why cannot his successors? And what happened to all the other jewels not even mentioned in the treaty? Dalhousie decided he would leave me with a handful and sold off the rest. Two catalogues of those sales are now with me. Furniture, shawls, plate, arms, and ornaments of the chase and war, even a likeness of my father. He then threw some into a prize fund for the troops engaged in the Punjab campaign. Prizes for troops come from what is taken from the enemy in the field of battle. I was not an enemy. For three years, all that belonged to me had been under the charge of the British to protect. How could they then turn it into a prize?

I have argued about all this for years now. If the Transvaal has been given back to the Boers, then why not my kingdom, at least my private estates? I could have still lived decently, had enough money to pay my debts, leave enough for my wife and children . . . The heir to Punjab's throne wouldn't have been forced to take out a gamekeeper's licence and sell live game and pheasant eggs to pay off debts.

Truth was on my side, but justice was not. So on the one hand they did not acknowledge the existence of my private properties and on the other, they continued to put forward the most egregious arguments regarding my pension. Any just man who reads the Terms will know that the pension of four to five lakh—40,000 to 50,000 pounds—was for me, that it was hereditary, that I could allot what I desired to my relatives and servants and that any lapsed payments would come to me. But all this cut no ice with the stubborn men at the India Office. They raised my initial stipend of 12,000 pounds to 25,000 pounds a year and left me to handle my life with that. And they were to turn the final screw with the condition that hurt most of all. All my estates were to be sold on my death. Nothing would go to my children. No amount of appealing to the Englishman's nobility and generosity and sense of justice has helped changed any of this.

And while I began to understand my situation, helpless and angry, my mother began to die. Her infirmities were claiming her, much before her time. Her body was succumbing to years of deprivation. I watched her strength ebb, her strong voice become weaker.

'You have taken care of me, Duleep,' she whispered. 'In my last years you have been my true son. I am fortunate. I can close my eyes in peace.'

'Please do not speak like this, Bibiji. You will be well. We will live together for many years.'

'No, my son. My time shall come soon. But do not lose heart.

Keep faith and you will be victorious. The Guru will guide you. But promise me, my son, that you will take me back to my country when I die. Do not leave me here in this land of firanghis. I will get no peace.'

And so saying, early one morning, she became silent forever.

John Login, autumn 1863, Felixstowe

Lena and I had just moved to Felixstowe to take advantage of the sea breeze. I had hoped that there I would also recuperate from a severe cold that I had contracted when carelessly walking one morning without an overcoat in Hyde Park with a mean east wind blowing.

On the first day of August, a mounted messenger rode up to our cottage with a telegram dispatched by the nearest office at Ipswich. It was from Duleep, telling me that Rani Jindan had died that morning. Though I was not up to the journey I left without hesitation, knowing how distraught Duleep would be.

The household was in turmoil with the servants expressing their grief, as Indians are wont to, with a lot of wailing and breast beating. Duleep himself was in tears and quite at a loss. He sat beside the body of his mother and kept looking at her face as if hoping that she would suddenly smile, or get up or begin to talk to him. He clung to me for a long while and I felt his pain as he sobbed against my shoulder.

'She has to be taken to India, my dear friend,' he said. 'That was her last wish.'

I had to make arrangements for her remains to be interned at Kensal Green cemetery until the journey to India was possible.

Finally, when all the permissions were in place, a solemn procession took us to Kensal Green and there I stood by the Maharaja as he addressed a group of Indian notables and servants who hunched together around a grey gravestone on which a simple inscription had been put down hastily in Gurmukhi with a translation in English: 'Jind Kaur, Maharani of Lahore, died the first day of August 1863.'

Duleep's sorrow made him put aside his natural shyness. With quivering voice, he spoke long about the strength that the Christian faith had given him, a strength that allowed him to face this moment of loss. I felt some satisfaction at my role in helping him find his path.

Lady Lena Login, winter 1893, Felixstowe

My dear husband, who so gladly shared the Maharaja's sorrow, was only destined to remain in this world a few days more. On the 18th of October, St Luke's Day, he finished his supper with me in the parlour, and walked up to sleep with a hymn of the Lord on his lips. Almost instantly and without a moment's pain, the Lord summoned him to Himself, leaving me, the children and so many others who looked towards him for sustenance and advice, forlorn and desolate.

So many dear friends wrote to express their sympathies, their high regard for John's life, his goodness. Her Majesty herself sent a most kind message. And on the day of the funeral, many honours were bestowed on my good husband. Old friends from India, John Lawrence, Frederick Currie and many others, came to stand by my family and me. Duleep was a chief mourner along with my children. He was truly distraught and made no attempt to keep to the restraint that the company of Englishmen had taught him.

As he rushed in, his first words to me were: 'If *that* man is not in Heaven, then there is not one word of truth in the Bible.'

At the graveside too, he gave utterance to his truest feelings, and those around could not help note the passion in his voice.

'I have lost my father!' he said.

I could understand it—after all, John had been his true and most faithful friend for fourteen years. In fact, he wanted to place John in a family tomb that he planned to build at his new property at Elveden. It was a great grief to him that my husband had not been able to see the estate. But ultimately he had to listen to my wishes that I would much prefer John stay at his eternal rest on top of the hill at Felixstowe.

'Then I will make his memorial here,' Duleep declared. He was true to his word. He had a most beautiful memorial designed and installed on my husband's grave, a memorial in red and grey granite and white marble, with a white cross that still serves as a beacon for sea-pilots as they come in. The Queen herself approved every stage of that memorial.

Duleep had another duty still to perform in that time of loss. He had to take home his mother's remains and scatter them on the holy waters of an Indian river. But such was his attachment to us that before he went, he again came to spend a week with me at Felixstowe.

'I know, Lady Login, that nobody can take Sir John's place for the children, but I wish to make them feel that there is someone who cares for them. I will go to India to perform my mother's last rites but I wish you to know that should anything happen to me while I am there, my will is made and the children provided for.'

He was lonely then; he had lost his mother and his trusted friend, my husband, within a matter of two months. By cruel fate even his secretary Cawood and his faithful manservant Thornton were summoned to the Lord in quick succession. I knew that he was in need of a wife. Soon enough he spoke to me about it.

'I know you were keen that I marry Princess Gowramma, Lady Login, but that is all behind us now. I search for a companion but I fear that I should end up marrying a worldly woman, a woman of English society. Whatever I have tried in this direction so far has failed and perhaps that is for the better. I do not want to be reduced to a social lout, going from one country house to another. I have no heart for such a life. And an Indian wife will no longer do for me. Where will I find someone suitable, a person of rank and also a Christian? All I yearn to do is to lead my life as a good Christian. I have been thinking a lot of this and I am convinced that all I need is a young girl whom I can train to live the way I want her to, who will help me in all I want to do.'

'But where, Maharaja, will you find such a person?'

'I will go to Cairo—on my way to India. There is a missionary school there. I will request the missionaries to help me choose a mate from amongst their wards. She will be Christian, and far away enough from England and India!'

'Please don't do anything in haste, Maharaja. It is a decision that will influence all else that will happen in your life.'

'I am serious, Lady Login, very serious,' he said. And then breaking into a sudden laugh, as was his wont, he continued: 'I can lay a bet.'

Quickly he put pen to paper and wrote out a strange memorandum, which I have hardly had occasion to show to anyone at all.

I promise to pay Lady Login £50 (fifty pounds) if I am not married by 1st June, 1864, provided my health keeps good.

Duleep Singh

N.B. That is, if I am not confined three months to my house, or ordered by my Doctor (of course showing a 'Doc' certificate) to go abroad.

Little did I know what all he would do to win that bet!

Duleep Singh, autumn 1893, Paris

Bamba, my dearest. Sweet and gentle Bamba. The wife who gave me my beautiful children and for many years, until my own demons began to destroy it, a sort of happiness. From this bed, from this barren shore before the tide takes me into the heaving deep, I want my thoughts to rest on her, on our sweet years together. I want to forget how I must have hurt her; I don't want to think of the dark time when we grew far apart, when she slowly became enveloped in a world of her own as I went away to fight my battles with Ada at my side. I want to think only of how, when we began our life together, she so often looked at me, with eyes soft with love, the eyes that first looked into mine when I had stopped in Egypt, on my way to India to perform the most painful duty of a son, that of cremating my mother's body and immersing her ashes in the holy waters.

My heart was vacant and aching and Bamba walked gently into it. She was so young, hardly fifteen and so innocent that I fell in love with her the moment I saw her at the American Mission in Cairo. I knew instantly that this was the girl who could save me from a dissolute, purposeless existence. There was something saintly about her. She seemed made for goodness. I knew in that instant that I needed her to anchor my life; I had been adrift too long.

I could not even talk to her without an interpreter. She knew no English and I had only a few words of Arabic. But I told her simply that I loved her and asked whether she would be my wife. The darling girl blushed, pink ... her name Bamba meant pink, I had been told. But she broke my heart then. She said she could not marry one so grand as me. Completely in love with her, I carried on to perform my sad duty in India.

But the poor dear girl changed her mind and I was overjoyed when I got a letter from the missionaries that she regretted her negative answer, that she had been sick and dejected since. I immediately sent some money and requested them that the arrangements be made for the marriage to take place at Alexandria. I sailed immediately after I had immersed Bibiji's ashes in the Godavari.

It was a beautiful, unforgettable day when I took Bamba to the British Consulate for the simple and elegant ceremony. Everything seemed fresh and new and exciting. Bamba looked so fetching with the orange blossoms in her dark hair that stood out brightly against her white dress. I could see her sweet face through the gauze veil as she read out the simple statement in Arabic.

Then we had a religious ceremony at the house of her father Ludwig Muller. Man and wife, we stayed for many days at the house I had taken in Ramleh, a few miles out of Alexandria. There I loved her and took care of her and watched her recover slowly from the jaundice that had attacked her.

There was immense curiosity and not a little consternation back in England, at the Foreign Office and at the Palace, about the strange oriental that I had married. I was in no hurry to tell anyone, having announced the engagement only to my friend Ronny Leslie-Melville and to my equerry Oliphant. Bamba was an illegitimate child; Ludwig never married her Abyssinian mother. To me that didn't matter—my father too had had many wives and some liars among the British still said he had never sired me. But it would have mattered to a lot of important people in London and would have been a great conversation piece for so many society ladies. So I took my time bringing her to England and introducing her to society.

Lady Lena Login, winter 1893, Felixstowe

I could not get over it for weeks! To go in search of a wife, carry out a courtship in the middle of a funeral voyage! And then return to tie the nuptial knot and bring back a bride in place of a coffin! This was one time when I wondered if we, my late husband and I, hadn't been part of an exercise that had fractured deeply Duleep's sense of himself. His mind had been damaged, perhaps, in some subtle way when he was but a child. What unlikely ways he had of looking for love and companionship!

My shock was obvious to the Maharaja when he came to meet me after his marriage. We were sitting by the fire in my lodgings at Hanover Square where I used to stay often.

'I told you I would win my bet, and I would have too if the issuing of public banns in Alexandria had not taken so long. In any case I missed it only by a week, but what is a week when one is talking about a marriage that is meant to last a lifetime,' he said, quite gleefully.

'Wait till you meet her, Lady Login, you will agree that Bamba was raised for me. She has married me for myself, not my rank. She does not even know what it is to be a Maharani, and what's more, she cares nothing for all the jewels I have given to her.'

I recall he was in great humour that day, breaking into peals of laughter as he recounted how he had proposed to Bamba in English and she had accepted in Arabic!

The reports that I had received about Maharani Bamba—for till that time, given my own indifferent health, I had been unable to visit them and meet her—were positive for the most part. She was remarkably sweet and innocent and better looking than Gowramma, with very fine eyes and a submissive disposition. In fact, I was told that if she was asked whether she would like to do anything, she answered: 'Maharaja wish, I wish!' Duleep from all accounts was quite taken with her, hiring governesses to teach her English and general knowledge, spending hours worrying about the kind of dress she should wear, the colours that would most become her and so on.

I was to meet her, of course, many times, and her children, and could not help appreciating for myself her lovable qualities. She was a true Christian and all who met her felt affection and respect towards her. A most difficult life she had, and not of her own making. Yet she handled it with dignity.

Duleep Singh, autumn 1893, Paris

She loved me truly, like a good wife. She bore my children and she put up with my troubles, and me, as she had vowed to. She waited patiently for justice to be meted out to me and meanwhile, she did what best she could do for the children while I lived my tortured life. And I was less than just to her. I spent a lot of time away from her, in London, obsessed by my battles with the government. I sometimes sought comfort in the arms of other women, women like Polly Ash. Those evenings in Polly's apartment, with me at the piano and she humming with me, walking up to me, putting her fair arms around my neck, bending down to kiss me, those evenings had a certain magic. On those evenings, Bamba was forgotten. And then, during the days that Bamba was weak and ill in Elveden, I found Ada at the Cox's Hotel in London. She was only a chambermaid, but there was something so gentle in her face, something so pretty that I felt I could not live a minute without her. I became oblivious to Bamba's condition, her failing health, her dependence on drink. But today when I say this, tears roll down my cheeks, helplessly. And I know it is too late even to apologize, because Bamba is gone now. She lies buried in Elveden, reduced to dust . . .

Elveden Hall, my home, my heartbreak. I liked it the moment I saw it as I rounded a gentle curve on the road from Thetford to Mildenhall. It looked as if it had been waiting for me, with its ancient flintstone church, in the middle of the open yellow rolling heath, with its stunted pines and twisted birches. I knew that area already; it was home to partridges and pheasants. And I could smell the sea in the air. I had an ambition then, to develop Elveden, once it had been extended through some additional purchase, into a fine shooting estate. Like Sadringham that had been purchased by the Prince of Wales, or Lord Walsingham's Merton or Leicester's fabulous Holkham estate. I wanted to lay out the estate for big shooting drives and leave the agriculture to tenant farmers. While the nobility came to hunt, the farmers could produce wheat, barley, rye and turnips from the sand and gravel and chalk that lay in that soil. But I was young then. I didn't know how hard it could be to make any money on the estate, particularly when the agricultural depression set it. My decision to nurture game would prove wiser than I could have imagined.

I spent thirty thousand—an expensive loan, of course—on doing up Elveden Hall. When I was finished with it, the house with its four-pillared porch, bay windows and its four chimneystacks looked quite different from the building I had bought from William Newton.

I was fond of that porch. Many photographs were to be taken there, photographs of our hunting parties, of Bamba and visiting ladies, of the children. I spent another thousand pounds restoring the stone church of St Andrews in 1869, doing up the chancel and the marble floor, the wooden arched ceiling with the carved wooden angels and the stained glass window at the back. I think ever so often of that church nowadays, perhaps because Bamba and Eddie both lie in its grounds. I know they would like me to be there with them when I finally die so that we can all be within sight of the house where we had so many good times, just across the lily pond that lies in the shade of the giant cedars.

The architect Norton worked on all the external changes but I insisted on having the rooms done the way I wanted. I wanted them to remind me of the rooms of my childhood in Lahore. People will say that I, the 'Black Prince' of Suffolk, wanted to recreate Lahore in my drawing room. To feed my fancy, or perhaps to console myself. I did not care then what people said, and I care even less now. From a set of watercolours of Lahore that I had and some photographs that I had issued out of the India Office, I showed Norton the Shish Mahal. I wanted him to recreate its double pillars and arches and most of all, its amazing walls inlaid with semi-precious stones and convex glass pieces that broke the light of the chandeliers into a million parts ... I had often sat there as a child, surrounded by courtiers, and watched the fabulous fountains playing in the courtyard. I can still feel the spray on my face—I would walk close to them on summer evenings, my palms outstretched to the rising water.

Norton did well. He managed to recreate much of the magic of the Shish Mahal . . . with little pieces of treated mirror in the plaster of the room, its pillars, the cashmere shawls on the walls. A huge marble staircase led up to the other rooms that too had their own share of arches and cupolas, quite unseen in this part of the world. I put in a huge fireplace in the library, topped with a massive mirror right up to the ceiling. I spent many hours in that room on the circular leather sofa in its centre. It took a while to finish it all and put up the furnishings. By that time Victor was getting to be a big baby, just beginning to talk, and Bamba was carrying Freddie.

When visitors came, for evening receptions or for the shooting parties, they all gaped and wondered at the interior of the house. They were charmed at the way the parrots greeted them, they marvelled at the hawks, falcons and monkeys. They would be transfixed by the huge painting of the Lahore durbar that covered an entire wall of the drawing room, with Maharaja Ranjit Singh sitting among the chiefs and the ministers, horse traders from Kabul presenting gifts, the warriors standing on the sides. That painting showed all who had mattered in the Punjab durbar and the visitors would make me point out each one of them and tell them the stories. And many evenings I would tell them of the killings that took place after my father died. I would tell them of the death of Kharak Singh and Naunihal Singh virtually on the same day, of the murder of Sher Singh and his son by the Sandhawalias . . . stories that I remembered from my days in Lahore, or from what my mother had told me later. It pleased me to see the wonder on the faces of my listeners, to hear their expressions of admiration. Today I realize that it must have seemed a pathetic attempt to regain some lost glory; I suppose there is always something pathetic about a king without a kingdom, and a man without a life he can call his own.

Maharaja of Lahore! Son of the Lion of Punjab! How empty it all sounds as I lie here. They say that people still wait for me in Punjab, that if I had managed to reach Punjab at the head of an army from Russia they would have welcomed me with open arms, forgiven me for forsaking my faith and going away to England. They would have remembered only that I was the son of Ranjit Singh, the last remaining light of a star that had sunk into a dark night.

But that was not to be ... and now, it all seems so unreal, so fantastic, that it is indeed a wonder that I tried ...

On such nights these windows seem too small. They are the windows of a prison cell. I yearn for these walls to crumble, so that my vision can travel untrammelled over the night. I am tired of walls. Now at least, when I no longer ask for anything, except to lie down and be one with my Maker, now at least let these walls descend.

Memories assail me like armies marching in the night ... the armies that I could have led but was never allowed to ... Memories, they come like a storm.

Memories of my childhood are strongest as I wait to die. They are fresh as a morning is, unburdened by the events of the day that is to follow. I remember the horses and elephants and my army of sixty companions, trained by me. Trays of jewels being brought to me every morning, to chose what I will wear for the day. Gold and silver coins to fill my pockets with, and I would throw handfuls when I went riding on my elephant through the bazaars. Being weighed every month against butter, grain and coins that would all then be distributed to the poor. Learning how to wrestle. Riding with my falcon on my arm, letting it go, catching him on my arm again.

Now I see Shivdeo playing with me, wearing his white turban and his string of pearls. Always trying to behave like me, always trying to run away from his mother. I tease him and he runs after me and both of us are running on the lawns of Martin's kothi in Fattehgarh. It is evening and as I look up there is a cloud of mosquitoes above our heads. And from the river, the sweet smell of melons. We want to run down to the river, through the narrow opening of the prickly hedge around the garden and past the white wall that has been newly built, but just as we are about to leave the lawn, I hear Login calling us back ... and the guards close in.

Fattehgarh, Mussoorie, Lahore—such distant days, in another world ... and yet some evenings they mingle easily with London, Paris and Moscow, and with memories of those happy unknowing days in Elveden, when the children were young and life still had something to offer despite all that I had lost.

The memories now swirl all around me, now gather and float away, past my window into the dark night. Soon I too will be part of the night, just a memory, a flake of human existence, an interesting story, a few dusty files in a library. All these matters with which I torture myself—of treaties and pensions and estates—will not matter to anyone, in a while not even to my children.

I wonder what the children will think of me finally. Whether they will understand that these battles I fought were as much for them as for myself. As much to protect their futures as to reconcile my past. I see none of them taking the battles forward; except sometimes I see a flash in the eyes of my eldest daughter Bamba. But not in Victor, and not in Freddie . . .

But Victor and Freddie made me a proud father whenever they went shooting with me. Both had inherited my quick eye. I have always believed that shooting came naturally to us, the lionheart's children. We got six hundred partridge one day at Eriswell and one afternoon on Cooksey Hill I saw Victor get two birds with his first gun and he had three others falling with his second before the first two had hit the ground.

Partridge was aplenty at Elveden, much more than pheasant. And many other birds nested there in the hundreds—Norfolk plover, ring plover, nightjar, crossbill, woodlark. Even some wild duck and snipe on the marshlands beside the river.

In those days, we still shot partridge by walking up to them. The gamekeeper would fly a kite that looked like a hawk over them and they would hide in the clover and we would walk up to them as they sat and empty our muzzleloaders into the clover patch. The rabbits were tricky. They have a very sharp nose and after a few shots they know where the guns were and they would run towards the beaters than away from them. I outwitted the clever creatures by building platforms up in the trees, overlooking the open spaces. They could not detect the guns then and came running straight towards us.

In the end, there was no doubt that Elveden became one of the finest shoots in England. What magnificent shooting parties there were! What meticulous planning! Timings fixed, drives planned and new fences put in to make the birds rise properly.

I enjoyed myself at these shooting parties and I loved the colourful sight, as colourful as the armies on parade in Lahore—the beaters with their white smocks and red collars and hats, the keepers with their bowler hats, brown suits and leather gaiters. And the sound of the keepers' horns directing the beaters, signalling to the guns.

This is a memory I like to keep close to me, with its smell of gunpowder and the scent of heather. It is one of the few things that still make my blood run.

A small, counterfeit life made up of small, counterfeit things. Oh yes, I know how history will judge me—only martyrs and conquerors are forgiven the faults of aristocracy and class. I only lived the life I had been taught to live, the life of an Englishman of rank, but without resources to live it properly. Perhaps if they had allowed me the resources, I may never have realized who I am . . . I even joined the prized London clubs, the Garrick and Marlborough and then the Carlton. Ronnie, my friend, was behind my joining the Carlton; it was he who made the Duke of Richmond put me up for it and I made it with support from Walsingham and Colville. Those were days when I harboured an idea that I could play a role in politics and Ronnie thought it the best way to go. Men at the club thought that I might try to stand for the seat at Whitby and in the process give a scare to Herbert Gladstone.

But soon enough word came to me that Her Majesty did not approve of my efforts to get into the House of Commons. I abandoned the plan, like I had abandoned the plan to study at the university or to go home to India. I had become used to the idea that my life would be planned for me, down to the last bloodless detail, and that there were things that I would not be allowed to do.

The Queen suggested that I become a Lord. But I was not interested. A king does not need a peerage. Yet after Disraeli came to office, he sent the Duke of Argyll, again at Her Majesty's instance, to Elveden.

His Grace talked to me in the library and told me that Her Majesty wanted to make Victor a Marquis and Freddie an Earl. But I had to tell him politely what I really felt.

'I am a Royal and I am not English,' I told him. 'We love the

English and especially Her Majesty, but I and my sons are, first of all, Sikhs. Such titles we cannot accept, no matter how kindly they are offered.'

It was for the same reason, I told the Duke, that though I used my coat of arms, drawn up by the Prince Consort and initialled by the Queen herself, I had no intention of registering it at the College of Arms.

The truth was that I was no longer fooled by all of this flattery. Late perhaps but I had realized how much arrogance and insult there were in these concessions. I read Prinsep's *History of the Sikhs*, I read the documents and files and Blue Books at the British Museum. I understood all that my mother had tried to tell me. I had not just lost a kingdom, but also a religion, a people, a way of life. Everything that could be home.

Arur Singh, winter 1905, Lahore fort

Arguments, justifications, pleading for money—that is what our Maharaja was reduced to for so many years. He was desperate for money and who could blame him? He was a father of six children; he lived as a man of rank in the manner he had been taught by the English themselves. He was the heir of one of the mightiest, richest kings of Hindustan.

He tried to explain his case to each new Secretary of State, men who had been only young boys, and some not even that, when he sat on the throne at Lahore. He appealed to their sense of fairness and justice. He had been taught to believe, after all, that all Englishmen, all Christians are fair and just. He explained patiently and logically but as the years went by, and no one listened, his patience too wore thin.

First was the matter of his pension. He believed that a provision of at least 40,000 pounds per annum was to be a permanent charge on the vast revenues of the state of Lahore for his benefit and the benefit of his successors. The government had only fixed a stipend of 25,000 pounds and that too only for his lifetime. The accumulated pensions that had lapsed due to death of his relatives and servants were not allowed to come to him. An amount of 105,000 pounds had been given from this account for the purchase of his property at

Hatherop but when that proved to be unsuitable it was sold. To buy Elveden and refurbish it, he had only been given a loan of 198,000 pounds, for which he was paying more than 5,000 pounds in interest out of his pension! Other heavy deductions on account of insurance premiums and pensions to the widows of Login and Oliphant further ate into his pension. His private estates in India had not been restored to him. In fact the India Office continued to deny the existence of any private properties.

All he got was self-righteous answers and sanctimonious advice. Be more careful with your money, he was told. We have settled everything there was to settle. There is no inequity. They tried to paint him out as an extravagant spender, an inveterate womanizer; in short, an oriental philanderer. A 'gentleman' of position, Colonel Sackville West, was appointed to audit his accounts. His report was clear: Elveden had no rival as a sporting estate of matching acreage. The land was being worked at a loss with understocked farms but there was no evidence of mismanagement. And there was no extravagance. The only excess was in the preservation of game. Our Maharaja knew that already. He had worked hard to preserve game on his estate. He wanted to shoot on his estate. He was a true Maharaja. But life had made him also a strange Maharaja who was also the owner of a game-dealer's licence. A strange Maharaja who was ready to work as a jeweller and diamond merchant! What else was there to do? The estate would not pay for itself. The agriculture market was down. The summers were dry and the harvests were bad, year after year. And the bills kept mounting.

The son of Ranjit Singh begged the British Crown to lend him money to pay shops, hotels and doctors. And finally one day our Maharaja could take it no more. He wrote to the Secretary of State that he would like to give up his rank. He wanted to dismiss all the menservants and reside economically. For a while he did shut down the estate and moved to Holland Park in London. He was preparing for the day when he would be no more and his children would live like ordinary people, having been done out of their inheritance by the government. The truth was that it no longer seemed the right thing to do to keep the rank of a Prince and sell pheasant eggs.

Duleep Singh, autumn 1893, Paris

It's that part of the day that I dread most, the hour before nightfall. The sadness becomes a physical ache, a crushing ache. I miss Bamba, I miss the children. I wonder what each of them feels about me today. I wonder if suddenly they got a wire that I had died in a hotel, in Paris, what each of them might do, how many tears each would shed. Bamba is gone, but she may have gone with the pain of having been abandoned by me. What else could I do? I could not go back to England after what had been done to me; I could not carry them along with me to France and Russia. There was no choice. But at this hour of the day when the greyness swells with the dark seed that will soon make it night, all this sounds less convincing. All that matters is that Bamba and Eddie are no longer in this world. The other children are far away and may not even be thinking of me.

I am alone, as perhaps I deserve to be. This fog of unknowing that I carry inside me, it is a curse. Who, finally, am I? What parts of me are truly mine? What vital flake of my heart was deadened and cut away that I am always on the margins of love, of understanding, of knowledge. I have lived in a haze of confusion, locked inside my half-self, set free only when a vision of grace and kindness, or plain seductions of the flesh, took possession of my heart and my senses. All the world and all happiness seemed then to contract to one moment, one face—Bamba, Ada, even Polly. Bibiji. Arur. But then my lax mind moved on. Perhaps my children would be right in getting over me too soon. My love for them has been feeble, there was always my own shadow that fell between us. But what was I to do? No, nothing was my fault. Nothing.

Lady Lena Login, winter 1893, Felixstowe

In the summer of 1883 I was surprised to receive a letter from the Maharaja wishing to pay me a farewell visit in Kent, where I was staying at that time. He said that he was done with England's deceitful bureaucrats and was leaving England for good. Since I had been living in near retirement for many years I had not been seeing him as much as in earlier years and was therefore unaware of his money troubles or the pitch of desperation that he had reached.

The first thing that he told me was that he had already auctioned off jewels worth about twenty thousand pounds and arranged passages for himself and his family to India.

'Please, Maharaja, do not act in haste,' I counselled him. 'This is an enormous decision that you are taking.'

'I am done, Lady Login,' he said to me. 'I am done with England and her hypocrisies forever. I am an Indian and I wish to go back to India, along with my entire family. They have to get used to Indian life. There is nothing left for them in England, though I have lived in this country like an Englishman. The government insists on selling Elveden Hall after my death. That is my home; it should go to my children. But I fear they will insist and my children will have nowhere to go. I no longer have the means to support my rank in this country, the rank that Her Majesty and her ministers gave me when I first came to England. Would your husband, that good man whom we both loved so much, ever have called this just?'

'You are right, Maharaja. John did not consider that the Terms of Annexation have been fairly carried out. He was always of the view that as a ward of the government, you deserved more justice than has been done. But I would request you again, do not act in haste. Allow me to take up, once again, your case with Her Majesty. I will appeal for her personal intervention and help.'

Despite his anger, the Maharaja's face softened at the mention of Her Majesty and his eyes filled with tears. Scarcely able to contain his emotions he agreed that the only hope lay in her direct intervention.

'If you say so then I am prepared to wait, Lady Login. I have always had the fullest faith in Her Majesty's kindness towards me. But I have no faith any longer in the men who stand between her and me. They are of a new generation. They do not wish to understand. They think my pleadings to be the rantings of an old buffoon.'

He stayed on the entire day and gradually lost the formality that had entered his manner. In the end he was relaxed enough to even start dancing on the gravel, despite his aching feet, to his favourite tunes being played out on the piano by my old sister.

Nearly forty letters on the subject, including many documents and copies of old exchanges passed between me and Sir Henry Ponsonby,

Her Majesty's Private Secretary, and some others, including men at the India Office. But I soon had to admit that in one respect at least the Maharaja was perfectly right. These men were not prepared to listen. As far as they were concerned, Duleep Singh was an irrelevant irritant living with his visions of lost glory. His pleas were not to be heard, his long memoranda were to be ignored, personal meetings with him were to be treated as mere formalities. They had all made up their minds and there was little I could do. Duleep stayed on in England for two more years, hoping in vain for some sort of settlement.

It pained my heart each time I spoke to him. He was deteriorating fast and I could see my husband's devoted work being unravelled. The feeling of being unjustly used was uppermost in his mind and gradually he was losing faith in everything that he had been taught, including the best tenets of Christianity. On some days, he would talk to me of preposterous things—of going to India to lead the Sikhs to fulfil a prophecy that his mother had told him about. He believed that he would get the aid of Russia ... I felt that his mind had lost its balance and in this state he would be easy prey to mischief-mongers and enemies of the Crown. And yet he retained affection and loyalty for Her Majesty in his heart. I could not blame him despite my pain. In truth, I had to admit that clumsy policies had resulted in giving him a huge sense of indignity and injury and were turning a perfectly loyal subject into a rebel.

Duleep Singh, autumn 1893, Paris

As the doors of England began to close on me, my own home, my country began to call. Visitors came uninvited to Elveden and then when I could no longer keep the estate open, to Holland Park in London. Patriots and emissaries brought news of Punjab, among them my own cousin Thaker Singh Sandhawalia. They talked of the inequities of the British Raj, the rebellion by the Namdhari sect of the Sikhs—Kukas, they were called—and how sixty-eight of them had been blown from British cannons. They told me that my people were waiting for me. All sorts of rumours, often contradictory, accompanied the visitors: I would be made ruler of Punjab and sent to fight against the Russians; I would assist the British to get recruits from among the Sikhs; I would be appointed Commander-in-Chief of the Sikh army; I would settle in Kashmir; on my return taxes and cow killing would be abolished . . . and so on.

Once again that strange prophecy, which some believed had been made by the last Guru of the Sikhs, Gobind Singh, was being talked about. I was no stranger to that prophecy. I was part of it. A man of my name was to be born and deprived of his kingdom. He would then spend a long time in a foreign land, marry a Christian wife, suffer persecution and be reduced to absolute poverty. Yet he would come back to rule the Punjab and lead his people to freedom. I had been told since my childhood that I was this saviour, but I had forgotten about all that nonsense until Bibiji, during her dying days, talked of it again. In disbelief I had asked her:

'How can all this come to pass if I do not go to India at all?'

'Mark my words, my child, I may not live to see the day but when the right moment arrives, circumstances will so shape themselves that you will be compelled to quit England against your will.'

The prophecy was all over Punjab again. And yet many dismissed it as nonsense, stories made up to suit the political demands of the day. Hadn't the tenth Guru said that there would be no mortal Guru after him, only the Holy Granth? Only sects like the Kukas believed in living Gurus. But Thaker Singh would not give up.

'It is true, Maharaja ji. You are the saviour. I have had the prophecy authenticated by all the principal priests of Punjab.'

Once again destiny, it seemed, was knocking at my door. And strange though it may sound, after so many years, and though I knew little about it, the faith of my ancestors began to call me. I wanted to know what I had given up. The survivor in me knew that if I were to have any sort of future in India, I would have to be a Sikh. My people may forgive what had happened in my childhood but now I would not be acceptable as a Christian. My cousin brought along two Bhais who could read the Holy Granth, and they read to me every afternoon, explaining the verses as they went along. I had not heard these verses since my very early childhood but somewhere they struck a chord—and yes, I will admit it—I felt the Guru's strength flowing in my veins.

I had seen enough of the Christian world, of their hypocrisies and cant. I had seen that when it really mattered they were like any other men, selfish, petty, scheming. Then what was there in that religion for me? It was better that I go back to what I was born into—an acceptance of the True One, simple trust and belief in the great architect of the universe who alone is to be praised and glorified.

My renunciation of Christianity would shake the Crown, I thought; it would amount to a negation of an achievement that they had long touted—an oriental prince who had found the Right Way. But what would they do when that prince turned around and said that he did not believe any longer in what he had been taught, that his eyes had been opened by the ill-treatment that he received at the hands of men who were supposed to have been, first of all, good Christians. One way or the other, the buzzing of a wretched little gnat would disturb the repose of the mighty British lion. The more they ill-treated me, the more my countrymen would believe in me. I would be a true Sikh, a martyr in their eyes. My life would have meaning, and I would earn the dignity appropriate to the son of Ranjit Singh.

Thaker Singh had already spread the word of my impending return and announced my intention to rejoin the faith of my fathers. He had travelled to Abchalnagar and offered prayers on my behalf. He had tried to enlist the support of the Sikhs of Hyderabad and Nanded. Purohit Harkishen Das who stayed with me in Elveden had taken five hundred rupees to offer karah parshad at the Golden Temple in Amritsar in my name and another two hundred and fifty rupees to offer at the samadhs of my father and grandfather. The newspapers in Punjab began to write articles about my return. At the Golden Temple—and I began to cry when letters came to me relating this—the priests prayed for my 'good health and Sikhidan'. The blessing of the Sikh faith. All this for me, who had turned away from the faith of my ancestors with foolish alacrity.

I vowed to take the pahul at Amritsar or at Abchalnagar. It would be a grand occasion when the King of Lahore would be baptized as a Sikh again after more than thirty years. A right royal slap in the face of the British government.

In any case, I had received the final ultimatum from the government, sanctified by an Act of Parliament. I could take forty-four thousand pounds and clear my debts but Elveden must be sold on my death and the money used to settle pensions on my family. The government was determined to break up my English home. My children were never to inherit what was rightfully theirs. There was nothing left for us in England.

I began to tear myself away from Elveden then; I taught myself to hate its very sight. It had become a bad sale by then, being good only for sale of game. I asked the government to appoint someone to take charge of it and do whatever they deemed fit. But that too they were not willing to do. What irony! They were now unwilling to support the dignity and scale of a life that they had encouraged me to adopt.

All I wanted to do was to go away. Sell Elveden, settle the money on my wife and children, fling the pension in the face of the government, rescind the treaty of 1849 and proceed to India as a Sikh fakir.

They were scared of that. Scared of the memory of Maharaja Ranjit Singh, whose name still lived on in Punjab fifty years after his death. The sight of his son could lead to open rebellion.

Sir Owen Burne, Secretary of the Political and Secret Department, tried to warn me off when I met him in January 1886: 'Picture me, Maharaja,' he said, 'as an austere Secretary of State. Suppose I was to say to you, "You are disobeying our distinct wishes by going to India. You will therefore be seized when you get there, you will be deprived of your stipends and be made to reside in some spot selected by the Government of India." What then?'

'I should laugh at you,' I told him. 'That is just what I want. You must at any rate feed and clothe me and my family, and my income will be then more than made up by subscriptions from every village in Punjab and from every part of India. Sir, I have resolved to go to Delhi, to resume my native habits and to bring up my children there.'

'I cannot understand why a nobleman like you, who has embraced Christianity, should want to go to India!'

'I have already taken the first step to abjure Christianity, because I no longer believe in a so-called Christian government.'

But despite my anger and my determination to go back to India, there were days when I did not want to leave Elveden at all. It was my dream. My children had been born there. They could have lived there after me, in the manner to which they had been brought up. I would sit on the bench near the pond from where through the brown and rust leaves I could see the gamekeeper's hut. I would let the low cold breeze that came up from the country blow in my face, hoping that it would sort out my jumbled thoughts, tell me the right way to go.

But I knew in my heart that there was little choice. England had shut its mind to my entreaties. My future, the future of my children, lay with the Sikhs of India. Even if there was nothing in the prophecy, I would at least be able to lead a life of dignity, give an estate to my children to live on after me, find suitable matches for them. Ordinary reasons, the reasons of an ordinary man, not of a king. So I sent the furniture and other effects at Elveden to the sale house and gave up my dream of my English home passing to my children. There was nothing left to do but to book passages for my family and myself to Bombay and this I finally did on the P&O Steamer *SS Verona* in March 1886.

Book Five

THE REBEL

Duleep Singh, autumn 1893, Paris

Aden. When I stood on the deck of the *Verona* and watched the jagged peaks come up on the coast, I had no idea that Aden with its still, turquoise water, unstirred by a single breath of wind, would become my last prison. There in that dreary port surrounded by broken black rocks, with its sandy streets down which the Somali boys raced their pony cabs, many things in my life were to change forever. I would embrace once again the religion of my forefathers. I would part ways with my wife and my family. I would never again go back to live in England.

When we had set sail from Gravesand, Bamba, the children and I in our first-class cabins, I had been consumed by a huge sense of relief. After all the agonizing, after all the indignities heaped upon me, I was going to India at last. Within four weeks I would be in my land and among my people. I would become one of them again. I would do all there was in my power to do in order to fulfil my destiny. I had told the government that I would go back and I was keeping my word and now let them do their worst.

I knew that they would not make it easy for me. That insufferable Burne, so polite and so devious, had been sent by the Secretary of State Lord Kimberley, just before we boarded ship. Solemnly he read out to me the instructions that he had been given by Kimberley. The infamous Regulation 111 of 1818—if I went to India, the Governor General could detain me any time. I was quite aware, I said, of these powers. Then he went on to make the most absurd offer—they would give me a sum of fifty thousand pounds to pay off my private debts on the condition that I would formally give up all my claims and promise never to go to India!

'Nothing shall induce me to accept this paltry sum that you offer me,' I told him. 'My claim to private estates alone is four hundred thousand pounds a year. I want none of your money. If this were not an offer from a minister of Her Majesty's government, I would treat it with the greatest contempt. And I shall never sign anything to renounce my claims or to give up my desire to return to my own country.' For fifty thousand pounds! Not enough even to pay off my debt to my bankers!

I also told Burne that it would not be easy for the government to arrest me in India.

'It shall only fulfil the prophecy, and that would then enable me to lead my own people. I am a fakir now,' I told him. 'I care little now for your money, or for my position or my property in England. I am all set to leave for India. I need to warn you and your colleagues that the policies intended to be followed by Her Majesty's government towards me are blind and suicidal. I am after all the son of an old ally of England. I am more than ever convinced that the prophecy of the Guru will be fulfilled and I will lead my people to freedom.'

On the last night in England, from the Great Eastern Hotel, I wrote to Her Majesty to thank her for all her kindnesses to me. And to my people in India I sent a one-word telegram: 'Started.' Nothing more was necessary. I had already written an open letter in the press in which I had told them that the Satguru, the true God, had blessed his errant child. Adverse circumstances had been created in England and I was compelled, even against my will, to go to a humble sphere in India. I had accepted His will, being persuaded that whatever happened would be for the best. I begged forgiveness of the Khalsa for having forsaken my faith and announced my intention of taking the pahul again. I also made it clear to them that I had no intention of conforming to the ills that had been introduced into Sikhism—such as caste observances or abstinence from meat or alcohol (papers in India joked that I did not want to give up my beefsteak and brandy-pani)—but would worship the pure and beautiful tenets of Baba Nanak and obey the commands of Guru Gobind. That letter had been my message to my people.

The letter became the excuse on which the Government of India hung its panic. It was an ultimatum, they said, and concluded that I would take advantage of the war between England and Russia were it to occur; in short, they labelled me 'disloyal'. True, all those thoughts had passed through my mind at one time or another in those troubled years . . . but they were not present in that particular letter to my people. The Viceroy, Lord Dufferin, simply did not want me on his hands in India—not in Punjab and not even in some remote corner of the country. But why did they fear me when many powerful Indian princes, men like Scindia and Holkar and the Nizam of Hyderabad, men of great wealth and with armies at their command, could move about in India freely?

I had thought that they may stop me at Gibraltar. But we passed the rock without event and continued to make slow progress through the beautiful blue of the Mediterranean, facing strong headwinds. There were many on board who were willing to spend their long evenings on deck listening to my tale—of my days in England, my problems with the India Office, of why I was going back with my family to a country that my wife and children had never seen and were probably not looking forward to. They watched me with curiosity and amazement as I began to wear my turban and Indian coats once we moved into the Suez. And then we reached Aden.

Brigadier General Hogg, who came on board at Aden, was clearly under instructions not to let it seem like an arrest. Later I learnt that the warrant for my arrest lay in his pocket that day, but he did not produce it.

'Your Highness, I would request you and your family to disembark and join me at the Residency,' he said politely as we stood on the deck.

I was not going to give in so easily. If I were to be arrested then I would have everybody know about it, all the people who were on deck, familiar with my story, and all the people waiting for me in India.

'I refuse to go willingly, Brigadier General,' I told him. 'My intention is to go to India with my family to start a new life. If you wish to detain me you shall, I am afraid, have to do so by force.'

'You leave me with no choice, Your Highness.'

The Brigadier General then reached over and tapped me on the shoulder.

'I have instructions, Sir, to request you and the family to disembark at Aden.'

I had been waiting for that. This was an official arrest. I turned to the passengers who were watching from the deck.

'Ladies and gentlemen, I told you this would happen to me. Now you have seen it with your own eyes. I am not being allowed to go to my own country. I am being forced to disembark. I, along with my children, am being arrested for some crime that I have not committed. This is nothing more or less than the compounding of injustice. But this matter will not end here. There will finally be a great State trial that will end in my favour. Justice will one day be served.'

It was heartening to hear all my fellow passengers cheer loudly as I, along with Bamba and the children, followed the Brigadier General down the gangplank.

Each day at the Residency hung heavy upon me. It was a strange arrest. I could go anywhere but to India. At first I thought I should go to Cairo and take Bamba and the girls with me. Victor and Freddie could go back to England. I could not bring myself to think of returning there myself. I wanted to write to my lawyers in England to check whether my detention was legal, but it would take them weeks to reply. I wrote to my agent to stop sending the rest of the baggage that was to have accompanied me to India. But these letters could not be sent. The Resident was under instructions not to let me correspond with the outside world. Whatever I had to do was now up to me.

I seethed in anger at being called 'disloyal'. I was fighting for my rights, I was fighting against injustice; I was not being disloyal to my Sovereign. It was a most hateful and false accusation.

'The address to my co-religionists,' I wrote to Dufferin, 'has been published from no disloyal motives whatever, but simply as my public renunciation of Christianity and to lay before my countrymen my bitter complaint against restrictions put upon my movements in India.'

As long as that term was not used, I told the Viceroy, during the exchange of several telegrams between him and me, I was willing to comply with what they wanted. Only, I should not be asked to refrain from going to India.

Hogg came and saw me often, whenever he had a new telegram from the Viceroy.

'Your Highness, as I had the occasion to say yesterday, the Viceroy too has asked me to convey to you the same sentiment: please do not consider yourself a prisoner. The whole of Europe is open to you and of course, you could continue to stay in Aden.'

But both of us knew the truth. I was a prisoner. A prisoner of a Brigadier General in the sweaty port of Aden, caught between two worlds, allowed neither to go back to my native people nor live with dignity and grace in England. I could not decide what to do. I would walk around the large shaded rooms of the Residency. Or I would sit in an armchair in the pillared lounge staring at the sea through the wide windows, open in the evening to catch the slightest breath of wind. And I would think. I would sit and plot and plan—how to get to India, where to go, how to get some justice in England, what to do with the children . . . And Bamba. Bamba with her long silences, suffering the heat badly, always worrying herself sick about the children, especially the younger ones . . . Would they have been better off in Egypt? Or should I send them to Germany . . . Perhaps England would be best for them, they knew that country, that was the only country they could consider their own . . . in that way they were more fortunate than I . . . I tortured myself again and again— Had I done the right thing so far? Did I have a choice that I had left unexplored? Was I being fair to my family . . . or to myself? And then as the evening settled in a sudden dark shroud over the sea and only the one flare from the lighthouse was left for me to stare at, I would pour myself a brandy and let all my doubts rest, for a while.

All of Europe was open to me, Hogg had said, holding the Viceroy's telegram in his hand.

'I do not want to go to Europe,' I told him. 'And how do you expect me to go back to England? For what? To face the open ridicule in the eyes of my peers?'

'Your family will be returning by the mail steamer this week, Your Highness. I would still implore you to join them and I am sure that if you agree not to try to go to India without permission and to give up political agitation, the government will give a fair hearing to all your demands.'

'Sir, I have waited decades for a fair hearing. I have only been tossed a few pennies here and there. I have had enough and that is why I set out on this journey. Enough of supplication and enough of hypocrisy. I will consider going back to England only if they promise me a full judicial investigation of all my claims by the Law Lords so as to give me full redress within six months. And if I am to give up my liberty and promise not to go to India without permission, then I must be paid a quarter million pounds sterling immediately.'

I did not need to be shown what they thought of my demands. 'Preposterous' was a word often used for whatever I wanted . . .

Oh how I wish that death would now come and shut out this world forever. A fire still simmers in my heart but there is no muscle to take it anywhere. Just life's regrets standing around my bed, like faceless men in black robes, haunting me, telling me what I should have done at what stage in life, which path I should have followed to avoid this misery and this pain. I tell them that it was not my fault— I was too young, I was too innocent. Their laughter echoes through my heart like in a hollow tomb. Too weak, they say. Else I would not have left the faith of my ancestors no matter what Login and Dalhousie said. I would not have followed English ways so eagerly. I would not have wasted days and weeks in idle pursuits, but fought single-mindedly for what I thought was right. If death comes now, it will take away these figures in black, all the failures and regrets of my life too will get some rest . . .

It was not easy to see Bamba and the children depart on the mail steamer, but there seemed little choice. Bamba wasn't taking the heat too well; the children were depressed and listless. Somewhere I realized that this was not their battle. I had to do this on my own. It would have been fine if we had managed to reach India. There they would have been able to begin a new life, as I had intended. But in Aden or in whatever city I might end up, they would forever be homeless.

As she walked away from me at the harbour that day, Bamba turned and looked at me once . . . and that look still haunts me. A look full of pity and accusations and love. She loved me true, and when that happens all sorts of things can get mixed up in one look.

Did I know then that I would never see her alive again, that our partnership of a quarter of a century was just about over?

I love you, Bamba. I love you like I always did—a dying man tells no lies—have you not heard that? Forgive me my transgressions and my sins. Do not accuse me of neglecting you and the children. Do not reproach me before the hour of my death. All I wanted was to make things better for you and the children after I was gone. I never thought that you would go before me.

Unknown to me, while one steamer took away my family, another one had brought two Sikhs to Aden. One of them was Thaker Singh—not the Sandhawalia, but another cousin of the same name, a cousin whom my mother used to trust and treat like her own son. Arur, my valet, informed me of their arrival.

I was allowed to meet them only in the presence of an English officer who could speak Punjabi. The Resident himself had come into the room and I could see his eyes watching my every move, studying every expression. I understood Thaker Singh by instinct. I could see in his eyes how happy he was to see me. I could see in them the anxiety of thousands of people of Punjab who had been waiting for me. I could see their frustration and concern as the news of my detention in Aden spread across the country, the disappointment of those who had left their homes and were already on their way to Bombay where the *Verona*, with me on board, was to have docked. It did dock, but without me . . .

I could restrain myself no longer. I moved a step, held him by the shoulders and hugged him and at last allowed my tears to flow freely.

'All of Punjab was waiting, Maharaja ji,' Thaker Singh said. 'From Lahore to Delhi, in all the towns and villages.'

I knew what he wanted to tell me. My telegram had reached Sandhawalia and all other important supporters. 'Started.' The word must have spread fast.

'Maharaja ji, the Guru himself has sent us here. A great duty lies on our shoulders. The purpose that could not be carried out in India can, with the will of the Satguru, be fulfilled here. We can administer you the pahul right here.'

'Here?'

I had always thought it would be in Amritsar or Abchalnagar, in one of the big gurudwaras, that I would reinitiate myself into the Sikh religion. I told Thaker Singh that.

'We too would have liked it to be in Punjab, Maharaja ji,' he replied. 'But, under the circumstances, we have come here to do our duty. Five Sikhs are all we need and any place can become holy.'

The thought electrified me. The moment that I had waited for was at hand. I could rejoin the faith of my fathers and wipe out the pernicious stain that I had brought upon myself by renouncing it for the faith of those who had cheated and humbled us. Then I had been a mere child, easily led astray, easily duped. Now in Aden I was doing everything with my eyes wide open. In one move I would tell the entire British officialdom what I thought of them. Being Christian did not automatically make one a good man. True, I had seen many good Christians, but I had also seen hypocrites among them. They had broken my heart. I had had enough of them. It was all over. I was repudiating their faith because of their own actions.

Arur Singh, winter 1893, Hardwar

It was my great honour, the blessing of the Guru, that I was chosen to be one of the five beloved ones, one of the panj piaras for the pahul ceremony. A Sikh trooper who happened to be on a ship in port and another Sikh from the colony were pulled in to make up the five. It was a blessed morning, Mangla Mai, the kind that one sees perhaps once in a lifetime, the moment when a man is reborn.

Thaker Singh ji read out the baani while we all sat in prayer. One of the men prepared the amrit as the prayers were being recited. As he stirred the sugar into the water in an iron bowl with the double-edged dagger, the Maharaja sat cross-legged before us wearing only shorts that reached down to his knees, his hands joined in prayer, his head bowed to the Granth. He took the amrit from Thaker Singh ji in his cupped hands and drank it.

Five times the Residency echoed with cries of 'Jo Bole So Nihal'. Then Thaker Singh ji sprinkled a few drops of amrit on my Maharaja's head and held him by the shoulders.

'Rise, Maharaja Duleep Singh, Sikh of the Guru!'

With tears in his eyes my Maharaja stood up and hugged each one of us. It seemed a new day had dawned, Mangla Mai; the Maharaja of the Sikhs was once again a Sikh himself.

Very soon after that he called me to his presence and gave me his command:

'Arur Singh, go to Punjab, go like an ordinary man, like a fakir. Talk to the people, feel their pulse. Spread the word that the people of Punjab are no longer without a leader. He shall come to guide them, lead them. See where our support lies. Try to find out who our enemies are.'

I left him then, to go as he commanded to Amritsar and Lahore. Far away from Elveden and London. To mingle with my own people, to prepare the way for my Maharaja to return.

But soon the oppressive heat of Aden began to get to the Maharaja. It weighed on his heart and he yearned to move to better climes. Now that he was a Sikh, he wanted Hindu or Sikh servants to cook his food. He needed Sikh granthis to read the scriptures to him every day; he needed a person to take care of the Holy Book. Seventeen servants waited in Bombay to join him and he wrote to the Viceroy to arrange their passages, but they did not arrive.

Finally, after the long hot summer, his strength sapped by the heat, the Maharaja decided to leave Aden on the mail steamer *SS Natal*. He wanted to go somewhere in Europe and take the waters. In one of his last telegrams from Aden, he told the Secretary of State that from the following month he was resigning his stipend under the Treaty of Lahore. He had cut all the ropes that had tied him down for so long. Now, clutching a slender hope, he decided to go his own way. Alone.

Duleep Singh, autumn 1893, Paris

I never did go for the German waters; Paris held me. Rebellion seemed to call me from every street corner. I felt free. Free of the terrible Terms of Annexation that had hung around my neck since childhood, the endless treachery and tricks of the India Office, the deceptive lure of my English life. And—I can admit this to myself now—free even of my family.

For the first time in my life, I felt that no one was watching me. How wrong I was!

I was now a rebel in every sense of the term. I would find enemies of the British and ally with them, no matter of what colour and creed they be. Russians, Irish, Germans, Turks, Egyptians . . . my enemy had many enemies and they would all be my friends. And there was a hope that one of them or perhaps all of them would somehow help me to do what I wanted to do so badly then—to get even, to go to India, to make the British administration in India come down on its knees, to make John Bull suffer huge expenses, much, much more than what had been so piously swindled from me by the Christian nation.

I found friends quickly. Men such as the Irish dynamiter Patrick Casey and the American, General Carrol-Tevis. I felt a certain sympathy in all of them as I told them my tale. Carrol-Tevis spent a lot of time with me right from the beginning and soon I began to trust him with all my confidences, even my correspondence. He was a man who had seen much—an American soldier of fortune who had fought in the Asiatic and Crimean wars and been in every battle, every conspiracy that I could name. And Casey shared plans that were exciting—of throwing bombs in the House of Commons, of blowing up the Tower Bridge. He did not want to kill a single innocent person but wanted to attack the symbols of empire.

Each evening I would leave my rooms at the Grand Hotel de St James et Bristol on Rue St Honore and walk towards the Church of La Madeleine in the pleasant late summer evenings of Paris, and I would feel the excitement of rebellion building up in my entire body. My mind would be on fire. At Reynold's Bar, where we all gathered, I would always be among friends, and ideas, plots, conspiracies would be traded across the tables far into the night.

General Carrol-Tevis, autumn 1893, Paris

I thought he was a simple man, foolishly simple. A muddled but good-hearted man, terribly in love with that young and rather superficial English girl who lived with him. She was the daughter of a gas fitter whom he wanted to make the Empress of India! So there you have him, a sensitive soul, suggestible, eager to please and to love. It wasn't difficult to win his trust. He was the kind of man who could very easily trust a stranger . . . and trust completely.

He was driven insane by his bitterness. He could say anything, might do anything. It was obvious that he needed careful watching. I watched him come close to the Irishmen, tell them his tale of woe every evening, and share all his plans, including his grand design of going to Russia. He was full of all kinds of nonsense about some strange prophecy in India.

'It has all been predicted long ago,' he would say. 'A saviour will come to save the people of Punjab. I am that saviour. I have become a Sikh again. I shall be damned, I know, but I shall have vengeance!'

I had to try hard not to laugh each time he said that. Some opportunists in India had obviously given him all these grand illusions and he, tossed aside and ignored by the British government, was only too ready to believe. He was looking for friends, for confidants and one only had to say a few things against the British Crown to make him start talking.

'I have letters from India, General,' he told me, showing letters addressed to 'His Majesty'. There were forty-five thousand Sikh soldiers in the British army who were ready to rise in rebellion if the Maharaja came to Punjab at the head of a Russian army. He did not need money, he said; the money would be collected in India!

After a few such conversations, Duleep treated me like a friend. Every letter he wrote or received passed through me. 'You are my Chief of Staff, General,' he said. I thanked him and began to pass everything to the Foreign Office in London. They were paying me a hundred and eleven pounds for the intelligence every month.

I am certain that till his last day on our blasted earth Duleep never suspected me of treachery. Some days he even managed to make me feel like a rat. But the moment would pass. Mostly, when I was not amazed by him, I was amused.

Duleep Singh, autumn 1893, Paris

Russia would welcome me, I thought. She could use me against the British. I wrote to the Russian ambassador in Paris, offering my services to the Emperor and requesting for a passport. I would then,

I told him, travel to St Petersburg in the hope that the Emperor would receive me and let me go to the Indian border.

The news that I was going over to the Russians reached Her Majesty quickly enough. And the letter she sent to me seemed still not without the affection that I had always received from her. She still talked of the days when I had been a 'beautiful and charming boy' and my lifestyle in England had been 'a pattern to all Indian princes'. She thought that it was the influence of some bad and false friends that had put wild ideas in my head.

I disabused her of that thought in my reply. No wicked friend or foe had put any notions in my head. It was the study of the records of the devious deeds of my English guardians as preserved in the Blue Books of 1848–49, the repeated insults at the hands of the Council of India and the Home government, and the most recent degradation at Aden that had embittered my feelings. Men are made desperate when there is constant injustice, cruel coercion—and all that her ignorant and insensitive ministers made no effort to spare me of. She had been gracious to me, I told her, and I would remember that to my dying day. But now, as a proud Sikh, I would not bend and would take all the consequences of my actions.

I made the mistake of showing Her Majesty's letter to Kotzbue, the Russian Conseiller de ambassade, when he finally met me.

'May I keep a copy, Your Highness?' he asked.

'I am afraid not, sir. That would not be correct on my part. I have offered you my services but she too has been my Sovereign.'

'I need to be able to explain to my masters your motives, Your Highness. What do you hope to gain by being in contact with Russia? Clearly, your bonds with England and its Queen have been old and affectionate. She is godmother to your child.'

'All that is well but I have had enough. I have decided once and for all that I will not return to England to bow and scrape before the government for what I believe are my rights. I only desire now to place myself under the protection of the Imperial Russian government.'

'And what will that achieve?'

'The British will realize what I am capable of. They will know that with the help of the Imperial government I can go back to India and all of Punjab will rise to welcome me. Let Russia give me only ten thousand men to appear on the north-west frontier of India and the thing is done. For there are some forty-five thousand Punjabis, my former subjects, in the British army at present, who would come over to me at once, and when other British troops are sent to oppose me, then the whole of Punjab will rise in their rear. And then there are my brother princes in India, who will surely make common cause with me, for haven't they suffered the same injustices at the same hands? The British may still not be ousted from the Punjab, but they may be forced to treat the Indian princes and soldiers better. At the very least this will even make them give me the compensation that I have been seeking. Three million pounds sterling and not a penny less will I settle for.'

'Surely, Your Highness, you do not think that the British would be simple enough to give you this amount of money without making sure that you will be loyal to them?'

'They will do anything to avoid the huge embarrassment that my return to India can cause them,' I said.

But I was wrong. The India Office continued to ignore me. And the Russians took the position, false though it may have been, that they were not interested in fomenting trouble against the British in India. With Casey's help, I had printed two proclamations that I wanted to send out so that all India may know what my position was, but I stayed my hand for a while.

My friend from my hunting days, the Duke of Grafton, and others were still working to have a Court of Arbitration appointed. If it happened, then I could have returned to my family with some degree of dignity and honour. But there was only silence from England and my desperation increased. I would have cheerfully accepted the verdict of such a tribunal even it had awarded me only a pice in damages. But they said they were powerless to appoint such a tribunal. Powerless!

Ah! What mockery! What falsehood!

I answered, then, by letting the proclamations appear in the press. In one, I set aside and annulled the iniquitous Terms of Annexation of Lahore that, to the disgrace of Great Britain, had been extorted by the unscrupulous Dalhousie when I was of tender age and ward of Christian England under the Treaty of Bhyrowal. And in the other, I sought the help of my brother princes in India, appealing to their oriental generosity. I did not mind appealing to them for money, for as I told them: 'We vastly prefer to suffer the greatest degradation, humiliation and shame of being a Bheek Manga or beggar before you, beloved countrymen, to being under any pecuniary obligation to such a most iniquitously unjust, tyrannical and foreign government, who though professing a code of high morality, piously swindled us out of our kingdom, and defrauded us of all our property . . .'

But somewhere in my heart I knew that little could be expected by way of help from the princes—Baroda, the Nizam, Holkar, Kashmir—all puppets in the hands of the English, as pliable, at least, as I had been made to be—though what was *their* excuse? Which of them had had their head and heart trained and tutored as children . . .

The Russians still did not budge. I told them that war between Russia and England would happen, whether they took on my services or not. The embassy wanted a million pounds before they would move my case with the Imperial government.

'Help me now,' I told them, 'and I promise that Punjab will pay a tribute of three and a half million pounds to the Czar when it is free.'

In my desperation I even wrote to the President of France, seeking French nationality so that I could go and settle down in Pondicherry. I promised him too that if I was supported I would spill the last drop of my blood in the service of the French nation . . . But there was no word in reply. Perhaps the Russians—and the French—thought that all I was trying to do was blackmail the British government into settling with me. Perhaps to some extent they were right.

Meanwhile, I moved away from the Grand Hotel de St James et Bristol to an apartment but this time I made sure no one knew where it was. All letters came care of the bankers, Mallet Freres on Rue d' Anjou. Even my father-in-law who landed up in Paris, and later even Victor, did not see the apartment.

I met the world at the hotels of central Paris.

Arur Singh, winter 1905, Lahore fort

I have read a lot about those times now. Perhaps he did not realize it fully himself, but the Maharaja had entered a very complicated world, a world of conspiracies and plots, of a secret League and the Great Game. And there was much more at stake than his personal war for justice. The European continent was under an armed peace pact fashioned by Bismarck—the League of the three Emperors of Germany, Russia and Austria. But this compact was not without its enemies. There were the revanchists in Paris, people who often met around the beautiful Juliette Lambert or Madame Adam, who sought revenge for France for its defeat at the hands of Germany and would do whatever they could to weaken the Emperors' pact and start a Franco-Russian alliance. And in Moscow, there were the Pan-Slavists, led by men like Mikhail Katkov, the legendary editor of the *Moscow Gazette*. The Pan-Slavists wanted to weaken the link with Germany and desired the growth of a nationalist Russia, taking under her wing the Slavs of the Balkans.

One of the crucial links between the revanchists of Paris and the Pan-Slavists of Moscow was a Jewish doctor called Elie de Cyon— E.C. He was a regular at Madame Adam's famed salon and the director of her political journal. He was also the Paris correspondent of Katkov's *Moscow Gazette*. It was E.C. who first took our Maharaja to Madame Adam's salon. The other guests and, far away, Katkov himself, must have listened to his story of injustice with great interest and felt the passion of his anger against the British government. Somewhere they must have also seen the possibility of using him to cause problems between the Russian and British empires that now stood eyeball to eyeball in Afghanistan, which in turn would mean problems for those in favour of the Emperors' pact both in London and in St Petersburg.

Through these evenings—at Reynold's Bar with the Irish enemies of the British Crown, or in fancy dress at Madame Adam's fashionable salon—my Maharaja nursed his own conspiracy. He sought help to get to Russia, to reach the Czar; he sent letters, through convoluted channels, to Punjab and Pondicherry to sustain his supporters. He did not know—nor did I, then—that he was under close watch, that all his correspondence was being read in London, that his supporters could be picked up one by one.

Duleep Singh, autumn 1893, Paris

Ada was at my side those days, more than she is today. I don't see her much nowadays. She is always away. With Victor, or on her own, or with one of her friends. She was my companion. I was, I am, so much in love with her. No longer just the passion that I had felt for her when I met her in the London hotel but love, tenderness, affection. A chambermaid she may have been, for me she was to be my queen. And those days in Paris, those days when hope fought against despair every hour, she was my closest confidante. At times just a child, innocent of the tortures that I went through, innocent of history, of intrigue . . . At other times a woman, such a beautiful woman that I forgave her everything she did or did not do—her ignorance, her selfishness, her expenses . . . I just yearned for her kisses, her embraces. Even when I was still at Elveden, with Bamba and the children, I used to think day and night of Ada, wait for her telegrams from London, insisting that she sent them twice a day even though they were just a few words to tell me that she was well. Then, when she joined me in Paris, my new, young, beautiful queen was with me day and night. There was nothing to keep us apart. I was alone, and free of all my loyalties—to the Crown and to my family and to Christianity. I could do as I wished: I had cut all my traps.

Nights of excess, too, in the Paris of those years, with so many people who would become friends, go-betweens, fellow conspirators. I do not fully know who was trying to do what and who was being used for what purpose. I met many people at the wild parties thrown by Madame Adam. The entire government came to her house, so did everybody who had a cause to follow. All in fancy dress. Those were evenings when I drank and danced too much and left when the others left, at daybreak. She liked me, though I doubt that she knew what I wanted. Everyone knew what she wanted—revenge against Germany and for that she would use anybody she could, most of all Russia.

General Carrol-Tevis, autumn 1893, Paris

I suppose E.C. thought that the Maharaja would be a great addition to Juliette Lambert's fancy dress parties. I knew all about E.C. He was committed to bringing France closer to Russia and he was Mikhail Katkov's man in Paris. And we all knew what Katkov was about—the chief advocate of war between Russia and Germany, of bringing all Slavs together. He was to become Duleep Singh's greatest supporter in Russia. But of course the Maharaja saw grander dreams than even the likes of Katkov did—though his aim never warranted so much noise and such big words. He had his delusions, that Maharaja.

Arur Singh, winter 1893, Hardwar

The Maharaja trusted me completely, Mangla Mai. He trusted me more than his own blood, more than his own sons and certainly more than that temptress Ada. Perhaps that Carrol-Tevis was another man he trusted, and in my view, he trusted him too much. I never liked that man; he was too slippery. He was an Irishman or American or something and I did not like the way he oiled his way into the Maharaja's confidence by meeting him every evening at the bar. I was suspicious of him ever since I saw him signing himself simply as C. Why would a man who had nothing to hide do that?

But my Maharaja was like that—a child with some people, opening out his heart completely, sharing his plans, ambitions, fears, conversations. He sent me whenever there were important missions to be performed. First, as I already said, he sent me to Punjab from Aden to wander from town to town like a fakir, eating what I could, sleeping wherever the day ended.

And when I joined him in Paris, he sent me away to London. He wanted me to go back and get his clothes and his beloved dogs. No one else could have brought those dogs across the sea. He took them all the way to Russia with him. They were precious to him, those animals, as were his hunting guns. These kings cannot give up their hunting, as you well know, Mangla Mai, no matter what other catastrophe happens in their lives. That way our Maharaja was a true king; he had all the royal passions.

Duleep Singh, autumn 1893, Paris

Each evening there was something to talk about, a tomorrow to drink to. I was part of all this, but my own aim was clear—to show down the British government and avenge myself. And if it meant that I had to get to the Russians and march with ten thousand Russian soldiers past Herat into India, then so be it. Somehow I had to get to Russia, to St Petersburg and to the Czar. Once I had done that, or so I thought, things would work my way.

And at the same time I told my friends in England that now I would not settle for anything less than three million sterling with the British government and they could throw in a peerage for me and a seat on the Council of India both in London and in Calcutta. That way I would have a handle on things that happened both here and in India. I also took from my resources in England all I needed. There wasn't much left, but it was all I had. I would no longer touch their stipend. Some last lot of jewels still lay with Coutts and I asked my solicitors to send them across with Victor when he came to see me in the winter of '87, the same winter as my father-in-law old Muller came to see me. They both thought it odd that I wouldn't take them to my apartment, but I was certain that I was being watched. I was too great a weapon in the hands of the Russians—if only they knew my potential—for the British to stop bothering about me. I also knew that I had a longer game to play. I still had my visions.

Arur Singh, winter 1893, Hardwar

When we needed to get out of Paris, I was the first one to manage to get a British passport, before either the Maharaja or Ada. We needed those passports if we were to travel to Russia—in fact, Russia and Turkey were the only countries one needed a passport for. We also needed a Russian visa. It was quite easy, actually. I simply went to the British Consulate in Paris and took with me a Frenchman, M. Genet. Soon we were sitting in front of the Ambassador himself. I told him that I wanted to go to India via Turkey.

'Why do you want to visit India?' I was asked by the Ambassador.

'Excellency,' I replied, 'I have a great desire to visit my birthplace in the Punjab. I have not been there ever since I can remember.'

And after a few other inconsequential questions, the Ambassador asked me a dangerous question.

'Mr Singh, do you not have someone else in Paris who could stand witness as to your identity and nationality, perhaps another Sikh, perhaps someone like Prince Duleep Singh?'

I looked him straight in the eye and said: 'Excellency, who does not know Duleep Singh? I too know him. But alas, I am not in a position to go to a Maharaja, a king, and ask him to give me a certificate of identity. Hence, I have brought my friend, a respected French gentleman, M. Genet.'

That was it. Before I knew it, I had a British passport in my hand. It was that easy! Sometimes I wonder how such a people have come to be our rulers—and of course how we, of a land so much more ancient than theirs, have allowed it . . .

My Maharaja went to Russia with so much hope, so much preparation. The embassy officials may not have been keen to let him go there but there were many important men in Russia who obviously saw some use for him.

I myself took care of thirteen trunks and two of the spaniels. Also, there were other boxes containing hats and all his papers, papers that he had put together to prove all his claims against the British, and even his precious pearls and emeralds. Ada also wanted to take everything with her. I don't think she had seen things like this ever before. She was not like Maharani Bamba, Mangla Mai, but what do I say. The Maharaja loved her so the less said the better.

Despite all that we took, we had to leave so many boxes behind in storage in Paris. I had to make sure that everything was put into the train in Paris safely. Only I knew what was in each trunk. We must have made quite a sight at that Paris railway station. But that is the way Maharajas travel and we didn't know how long we were going for. If all went according to the Maharaja's plan, we would never have come back to Paris at all. We could have gone on from St Petersburg to Punjab, to Lahore and Delhi. We could have gone on from exile to kingship. Everything then still lay in front of us.

That Irish friend of the Maharaja, Casey, came to see us off at the station. He was unlike many of the others who were frauds, imposters. He was a real revolutionary against the British. He had exploded several bombs against the British authorities. And he was one man who had truly come to our assistance. He had seen the true anger in the Maharaja against the British and had recognized a friend. He had gone to the British Embassy and got a passport for himself and his wife, just a piece of paper with their names and no photographs, that he had given to the Maharaja and Ada. That is how they could travel to Russia as Mr and Mrs Casey. That precious passport the Maharaja put in a leather satchel that he hung securely around his neck. That satchel also contained many more valuable things—a lot of money and letters of introduction to many important people in Russia from the Maharaja's friends in Paris.

General Carrol-Tevis, autumn 1893, Paris

I had already cabled the Foreign Office in London about Duleep's plans to go to Russia, though I must admit that I did not fathom the deception of that cad, Casey. I thought Duleep and Ada were to travel under the assumed names of Mr and Mrs Reginald Lorraine. That was what we had decided—the Maharaja, Casey, E.C. and I. He was to travel through Constantinople but at the last minute he became suspicious.

'There are plans afoot to assassinate me,' he said. So we all decided that it was better he travel by the railway. But till then 'Mr Lorraine' did not have a passport.

Much later—and I had some explaining to do for that—I came to know that it was Casey who went and got a passport in the name of himself and his wife and gave it to them. This was one thing Duleep did not tell me. Before he left, Duleep gave me one more letter for his cousin in India. He told him that he would soon be on his way to St Petersburg and the agitation must be now renewed with great vigour in Punjab and in India. Once again he asked that the princes of India be asked to subscribe money to raise an army at the frontier for things would come to a head very soon.

I sent a copy of that letter to the Foreign Office in London but

I earnestly pleaded with them that no action be taken regarding Duleep travelling to Russia on a false passport. He would hang himself if we gave him enough rope and only by leaving him alone temporarily could we get to the bottom of what, I was convinced, was a formidable conspiracy. He had promised to tell me everything as he went along and I would be able to unravel all the threads that led to his supporters in India. It would be wise, I had written, that we wait to see how Russia reacted and how Duleep compromised himself even further.

Arur Singh, winter 1893, Hardwar

Things started to go wrong very early in our journey to the east. Maharaja's satchel got picked at the railway station in Berlin where the train stopped for a long time. They were adding German wagons there and they were also changing the engine. We spent a few hours in the restaurant on the platform. I had been watching the train from the door with one eye and my other eye was on the Maharaja and Ada as they sat at a table, drinking coffee. I could see the leather strap of the satchel stretched across the Maharaja's chest. But something happened when the bells rang on the platform and passengers quickly moved towards the wagons. It was all so quick. Everything was lost, including the passports. God knows who the thief was, some gypsy or some intelligence agent, but he made such a clean cut with a knife that no one saw or heard or felt a thing. The Maharaja was certain it was the job of a British detective but he would not give up the journey. The train moved away from Berlin and we were still very much on board.

I thought it was the end of the story. Those Russian policemen in their grey overcoats were forbidding men and there was no hope at all as we stood in front of the desk of their chief officer in a room with a huge log fire. The Russians guarded their empire closely. They were suspicious of everybody; their Czar had already been attacked more than once. Everything was being checked—the train, the baggage, the documents. In fact, the train has to change wheels at that border because the railway lines in Russia are broader than the ones in Europe. How would we ever get across that border without the Maharaja's passport and visa? But the Maharaja was not going to give up easily.

'My name is Patrick Casey,' he told the policeman. 'And this is my wife. I have to go to St Petersburg and Moscow. Many important people there know me. Unfortunately my passport has been stolen.'

The policeman looked disbelieving at first. He looked closely at me as I stood silently behind the Maharaja. He looked at Ada and she gave him back an angry stare. Then he looked at the two dogs in their winter coats and he looked at our baggage. Once again he looked at the Maharaja, who had dressed up formally for the crossing into Russia. He wore a turban, with his pearls and one of his embroidered jackets, the like of which had probably never been seen in Russia before. Something made the police officer think twice and he asked the Maharaja to explain exactly who he was and what was his purpose in going to Russia.

'I cannot tell you my exact purpose. Except that very important people in your country know it. I had letters from Monsieur Elie de Cyon in Paris to Monsieur Katkov in Moscow and to many other dignitaries but these have been stolen. If you like, this can be confirmed with those gentlemen.'

The policeman told us that we would have to wait for twenty-four hours while he checked up. Telegrams were sent in different directions while we waited at that strange station with a strange name. I of course cannot even try and pronounce it right. Verjbolovo. You cannot pronounce it either, Mangla Mai—Verjbolovo! And every time I tried to pronounce it, the Maharaja laughed loudly and Ada gave me one of her usual irritated looks, so I stopped trying . . . Anyway, once the telegrams had been sent, the Russians became friendly and comfortable and asked us many questions about our dress and so on. I think they thought that we were a party of acrobats and Ada was a fortune-teller travelling with us. We laughed about it in the restaurant on the platform where we spent most of the day. Little did they know that the man they thought an acrobat was the last king of Lahore—and who could have been the king of all India—and the fortune-teller was his second queen. And as for me, I didn't care what they thought of me. I was happy to be where I could serve my Maharaja.

Duleep Singh, autumn 1893, Paris

Lost passport or not, I was not going to stop. I had been stopped once at Aden; this time I was determined to carry on. In the event I entered Russia in style. My friend E.C. got to Katkov and within hours the amazed border guards got a telegram from no less than Prince Dolgorouki, the Governor General of Moscow himself, to let us in.

And once I was in Russia I was hopeful that Katkov would get me to the right places. He proved to be a true, brave friend. He was a great and powerful man, old and yet young, full of courtesy, possessing a kind heart. He had handed over my letter to the Czar, who, I was pleased to hear, remembered that I had once, long ago, been presented to him by the Prince of Wales.

That letter of mine was important. I told the Czar that I sought no personal gains but only freedom from British yoke for my countrymen. My brother princes would rise with three hundred thousand men if I were allowed to accompany the Russian Imperial army to the Indian frontier. The Sikh soldiers in the British army would revolt; my people, the brave and proud people of the Punjab, would rise to cut railway and telegraph lines. Conquest would be made easy. India would prove to be a gold mine for the Russians, I wrote, just like it had been for the British. Three million pounds would be given to Russia as tribute though this could rise later to ten million pounds and millions more in trade profits.

Katkov had placed that letter in His Imperial Majesty's hands and assured me that my affairs were in good hands in St Petersburg. But he also told me that the Russian Foreign Office, headed by the pro-German de Giers, was opposed to me. He did not want to upset the existing balances by annoying the British.

Ha! Such caution about the British! The British Resident in Moscow kept thinking I was Casey. And they could not figure out who Arur was. They even thought that *he* was the Maharaja Duleep Singh! Bumbling fools! They found out the truth soon enough and went to complain to the Russian Foreign Office. There was hell to pay there, I suppose.

General Carrol-Tevis, autumn 1893, Paris

He really was convinced that it was all about him. Ah, the fatuousness of *mon Prince*! What he did not realize was that he was only being used by us to discredit Katkov and others, like General Bogdanovich, who were itching for a war between the Russians and the British. The British government could embarrass the Russians by accusing them of sheltering enemies of London—be they self-avowed rebels like Duleep or dynamiters like Casey. And the Russian Foreign Office could use that to put down Katkov's cabal.

So we were playing much bigger games even as Duleep sat in Hotel Dussaux with his pretty chambermaid, whom, incidentally, he kept busy by buying her a sewing machine. In the beginning he was optimistic and happy. While he waited for the Russians to decide his future, he dreamt of shooting grouse in north Russia or woodcock, snipe and wild fowl in the Crimea. I used to find it very strange, the way he would go from planning a rebellion to planning a hunting trip. Only a strange oriental mind could think like that.

He wrote to me regularly from Moscow, asking me to forward several letters. I continued to copy all those letters to London. The net tightened gradually around all those in correspondence with him.

Duleep Singh, autumn 1893, Paris

My letter to the Czar had at least ensured my liberty and safety in Russia and I was willing to be patient for the rest. For a while, my spirit was in seventh heaven.

But then fate dealt a terrible hand. The good God decided to take away Katkov. Once he was gone—and I still believe that he was poisoned by his many enemies—there was no one to guide me in that vast empire and I feared day and night that any intrigue in high places could have me thrown out of the country in an instant. I mourned him with thousands of others in Russia for whom he had held out a brave hope.

With his passing, hope began to vanish for me, too. I persisted with the Russian Foreign Office but there was no answer. At the same time I tried to ensure that England did not forget me. I wrote to the *Daily Telegraph*, hoping they would publish my story and thus respond to *The Times* that had launched a vicious campaign against me. But they did not. So much for their much-wonted fair play. The thought struck me that my campaign may be better served by American newspapers, such as *The New York Times*.

But first I posted my unpublished letter to several notables in England, including Her Majesty's daughter, now the Crown Princess of Prussia. Let her read, I thought, how the young boy whom she had met at Osborne on the Isle of Wight thirty-two years ago, when she herself was a child, had been turned into this rebel by the government of her illustrious mother—by its injustice and arrogance hidden behind a veil of Christian morality.

Let her read, I thought, and let her also tell her mother.

Katkov's death was followed by another blow, in that late summer of 1887—the death of my cousin and greatest supporter, Thaker Singh Sandhawalia. When the telegram from Pondicherry reached me, I felt like my right arm had been cut off. What was I to do without him? True, there was still his son, Gurbachan Singh, who wrote to me and to all others who mattered that he would carry on his father's work. But I had to fight hard to keep my spirits afloat.

Ada was waiting for our baby. She was worried about it being born in a foreign country and she was keen, as any girl would be, that her mother join her. She would not let me go anywhere, even when I was invited by the Governor of Tiflis to move to the south of Russia, nearer the Indian frontier. I hated being trapped in that estate in Petrov Park. It wasn't easy living. I had to do a lot of work around the estate, small as it was, and that tired me. I would think of the number of people who used to work for me on the estate at Elveden . . . and in Petrov Park not even Arur Singh was around to help me out.

Arur, who should have been my son. I think I told him that once . . . I had sent him away again to India, to collect money and not to return unless he could with a sizeable sum. I needed the money—everybody I talked to wanted money. The Russians were not interested in Indians and India; they were interested in my money. The Russian diplomat in Paris had asked me for a million pounds, and

since then there had always been the need to bribe officials at every
stage.

Arur carried letters from me—to Oudh, to all the native princes.
But he had been picked up, as I found out a little later. Obviously
some spy had come to know of his plans. The poor loyal man was
arrested and jailed and interrogated. And I am proud that he did not
let out too much. That's what he told me when he came back to me
more than three years later. Sandhawalia's loyal servant Jwala Singh
was also picked up when he went to Hardwar to immerse his
master's ashes in the Ganges. And another servant—Sohan Lal, I
think his name was—he too was arrested while sending letters to the
five Sikh states to tell them of my coming.

Arur Singh, winter 1893, Hardwar

'Get money,' my Maharaja commanded me. 'Go to India and do not
come back to me until you have collected enough money to make
the Russians believe that the Indian princes and people are with us.
We have to make it worth their while to take on the British lion for
us.'

What a journey it was, Mangla Mai. It cost me more than a
hundred pounds. Across the vast plains of Russia, frozen, piled with
snow and ice. I travelled day and night in Russian trains until at last
I came to the warm port of Odessa. I changed one ship after another,
German ships, others, and went to Constantinople, the great city
where the East meets the West and then through that new canal
which they have cut through the earth, the Suez. What a marvel that
is! Then I came down to Lanka.

After that it was easy. I stayed several days with Sardar Thaker
Singh Sandhawalia in Pondicherry and we talked at great length. The
Sikhs there had been waiting a long time for the Maharaja to come
across the seas; they had waited in vain. But when they saw me, there
was new hope in their eyes. I told them that the Maharaja had
handed me very crucial documents. I had his message to his brother
princes . . . ah these brother princes—they did not have the sense to
support him, they have been fattened too much, this Kashmir and
Holkar and Hyderabad. He wrote to them several times, telling them

that he would come to India, that he would deliver them from the yoke of the English. He wanted them to have their armies ready, should the need arise. He wanted them to let him know, through me, a mere servant—that is how much he trusted me—whether they would support the Russian Czar.

And there was all that business to perform with the Bengali editor, Shashi Bhushan Mukherji, whom the Maharaja had paid to publish his letters in his English newspaper. How was I to know that he was no longer in Chandernagore, that the newspaper had not been published in almost a year? Even Sandhawalia did not know and Pondicherry is closer to Chandernagore than Moscow or Paris.

So, Mangla Mai, you see, I had much important work to perform. I even had to make arrangements for the visit of a Russian officer who we hoped would follow not more than a month after me to check out all the information that we were giving the Russians. And I was to go to the Golden Temple and tell the Sikhs that when the Russians came with our Maharaja, they were to rise and cut the railway lines ...

The only mistake I made was to believe in that Bengali inspector when I reached Calcutta. I thought he was one of us. And he was a clever man. He made me speak a lot by pretending that he did not believe me.

'How do I know, Sardar sahib, that you are truly who you say you are? How do I know that you are not a British agent?'

'I am not a British agent, Babu. I am a trusted man. See what I have with me.'

Then I showed him all that the Maharaja had entrusted to me. Foolish man, that's what I ultimately am. A simple peasant, unfit for all this politics. I showed him the letter to the Bank of Bengal with the Maharaja's own signature. I showed him the cheque for five hundred rupees, the French notes. And then I showed him the letter to the Padshah of Oudh in which the Maharaja had written that though they had both suffered in similar circumstances, Oudh was still in the hands of the enemy but Duleep Singh had reached the great empire of the Russians and from there he hoped to come to India soon and help place the Padshah once again on the throne.

As my trump card I showed him the letter written by that Tevis, signed only with the letter C, that included some news articles from England that showed that the British government was shocked that Duleep Singh had reached Russia. There would be war with the Russians and then God knows what role the Maharaja would be able to play.

The inspector got excited when he read about the plan to set up an Irish military colony near the Indian frontier—here all the disaffected Irishmen in the British army would come and would act as ordered by the Russians or even ride for Duleep Singh.

'I believe you, Arur Singh,' he said. 'You are one of us. Come with me then.'

He tricked me into getting into a ikka gadi and took me straight to the detective department. I saw the gates closing quickly behind the ikka gadi as we entered that compound and I knew that the game was up. I felt wretched, not because of what was to happen to me, but in getting caught I had failed our Maharaja who still sat in hope in cold Moscow, waiting.

But they got nothing from me, no matter what they did to me. I can come and face you today, Mangla Mai, because I did not speak a word that could harm him, not a speck of information. I taught the Angrez what it means to try and break a Sikh. Even a Sikh whom they might have considered soft, simply because he had not stayed in Punjab but in Europe for full nine years, serving his Maharaja. They might have thought that a life in Vilayat, a life of soft beds and soft clothes, had softened my spirit. How wrong they were, Mangla Mai! I was one of the Khalsa and that is why the torturers could not break me.

A man called Henderson came down all the way from Simla to Calcutta to interview me. A large red-faced man with the most piercing blue eyes that I have ever seen. He was obviously an expert detective; he seemed to know a lot about me, a lot about the Maharaja. Four times he interviewed me, questioning me two, three hours at a time. Thrice we were alone in that small police cell and the fourth time there was a Muslim with him. Each time we went through the same things and each time I knew where I was to stop.

'Why have you been sent to India?' Henderson asked me, and his blue eyes seemed to make holes in me.

'My Maharaja commanded me to come. He told me—Go, Arur Singh, and raise money for us in India. And do not show us your face until you have raised a large sum.'

'Does he not get money from the Russians? Or from his wife? How does he live in Moscow?'

'He refused to accept money from the Russians. He told them it would come from his subjects in India. And the Maharani sends him not a pound. He lives because he has enough jewels to sell.'

'Has he got money from India?'

'I would not be here if he had. I have been asked to collect the money for him.'

'Who were you to meet in India?'

'I was to meet the Bengali babu, Shashi Bhushan Mukherji. He would tell me what to do next. He was to tell me how to raise money.'

'Who else?'

'I was to also go to Lala Jhinda Ram of Multan. He too had made promises of raising money.'

'Why did you go to Pondicherry then? What did Thaker Singh Sandhawalia tell you to do?'

'Nothing, absolutely nothing.'

'You stayed a fortnight there. What do you mean nothing?'

'He told me that no plans had yet been made. His agent had still not returned from Punjab.'

'Who was the agent? What had he gone for?'

'One Jwala Singh. His business was to find out things for me, to see where I should go. That's all I know.'

'Why did you go to Hyderabad?'

'No particular reason.'

'Did you meet any Sikhs?'

'Nobody of any importance.'

'Then why did you go?'

'I wanted to see the Nizam.'

Henderson did not believe me. In fact, he laughed right in my face.

'The Nizam would see *you*? You believed that?'

'Why not? I am the ambassador of another king.'

'Yes, of course. And did he?'

'No, I met some Sikhs who told me that it would not be possible, so I left.'

'What else do you know about the people who are to help Duleep Singh or the Russians?'

'I know nothing else.'

'You know more; we have reports,' said that Henderson, waving some papers in my face. 'Reports that you have met more people. You have already visited a man called Babu Nilamber and a man called Ghosal in Calcutta. Who are these men? What was your business with them?'

'I have not met any such people. I do not know anything else.'

'What had Shashi Bhushan told you?'

'Nothing, really nothing.'

'Arur Singh, you will go to jail, you will not be able to go back to Paris or Moscow or even your home in Kohalli. But if you tell me more, I can help. I can get your imprisonment shortened, even set you absolutely free.'

'But I know nothing more. What can I tell you?'

I could see Henderson was at the end of his patience. I had convinced him that I was a stupid man who knew only what he had already admitted. He was keen to go back to Simla and so after four interviews I was questioned no longer. I was put on a mail train to Chunar fort. I spent three years in Chunar fort, tortured and questioned many times by English policemen and detectives. I could show you the marks on my body, but you believe me, Mangla Mai. I did not betray the Maharaja or our cause. You have heard of Chunar fort before, our Mai Jindan too was kept there, so many years ago. I was honoured that I too had reached the same prison as her. I had never seen her. I was too young when she died in England. But at Chunar I often felt that I was near her, that she was telling me not to give in to the English, to protect her son, to do everything in my power, to use every bit of courage that Guru Gobind had given me, to fight for the rights of her son and to restore him to his glory.

Duleep Singh, autumn 1893, Paris

But the great European war, the war that would have put England and Russia on opposite sides and made me of real value to the Russians, that war did not come. The idea seemed to have died with Katkov. Instead, there was a wretched peace.

And there were others vying for Moscow's attention. There was the Kashmiri Abdul Rasul with his obsession of a rebellion by all Mohammedans from India to central Asia. He wanted to ally Turkey with Russia and me to be part of it all. He said that if Russia and Britain went to war, he could get the Egyptians to shut down the Suez Canal. I wasn't ever sure of his loyalty to the Sikhs or to me personally and Ada did not like him at all, with his one eye and fierce scar across his cheek.

And there was the Afghan, Jamal-ud-din. I had nothing in common with him. Though the Russians seemed taken with him for a while they did not forget me completely. I was told that I could live wherever I liked in the empire without a passport, that my heavy baggage could come from England and so on. To some extent I felt accepted. I may still be useful, someone must have realized.

That was also the year of life and death. My Bamba passed away suddenly. Weak and exhausted, she gave up her life even while caring for sick Sophia. They took her from London by a special train and buried her in the Elveden churchyard. By the time I got to know, the funeral was already over. My heart was heavy. I could do nothing but sit in faraway Russia and grieve.

For me Bamba was the only true comfort of my life, though I, restless of heart, demanded too much of her—duty and passion in equal measure. My poor, sweet-natured Bamba . . . The world may well think that I deserted her and the children, that I broke her heart by going away with Ada. And today as I am about to die myself, I know what it is to have a broken heart inside one. I am glad she is resting at Elveden. That was in many ways the only happy home that she had ever known. And I had only left because I had to, because there was no way I could have continued staying in England. It is true that I had placed a notice in *The Times* that I was no longer responsible for any debts that the family incurred in my name. But this was after I had resigned all the property in England for the benefit of Bamba and the children. And, since her father had insisted so, also half the income from Elveden estate. I had made sure the India Office paid them, too.

But this was not enough—for the children of royalty, even of royalty with no kingdom to its name, no amount is really enough. Victor was running up debts at the card tables, thousands of pounds. He even asked me for the money that lay for me at the India Office. I told him that I had repudiated the Terms of Annexation. I could no longer accept that stipend. I could not be bothered with matters connected to England. My English life was over as a dream. I did not care if he paid his debts or not, I wrote him; once he came of age, he would be able to, somehow. Meanwhile, if he wanted to retain my affection, I told him, he had never to ask me to humble myself before my bitterest enemy. I could not do that, could not disgrace the name of the Lion of Punjab. He fought with me, my eldest child, but I did not give up. I would not negotiate.

In the winter that followed, when we had moved into a cheap hotel back in Moscow, within sight of the Kremlin, a day after Christmas, Ada, after some amount of trouble, gave birth to a daughter. We named her Pauline.

Those early winter days in Moscow, just before Pauline was born ... they had a certain smell, a certain feel that I have never found elsewhere. Often I would sit by my window in the hour before the evening, looking out. I would wait for the moment that the lamps on the streets were lit, one by one, each yellow-blue flame throwing its own private circle on the fresh young snow. Every once in a while, a couple would walk across that circle of light, only enhancing my feeling of loneliness. Ada would be out most of those evenings, or lying down, trying to give rest to the baby in her womb. Once in a while, quite unknown to her, I would walk out into the snow. I would feel each step under me, balance myself against the slipperiness of the surface, and in that act alone there was a peace, a calm. On occasion I would reach the river that ran through the heart of the city. I would catch it on the other side of the Kremlin and walk along it, past the cathedral with its onion domes and past the bridges, just letting my mind float along with its waters, without target, without objective, without aim. Just float and rest and bump and float again . . .

Sometimes on these walks a great clarity would descend on my mind. All my doubts would be blown away by the cold wind. Then I would walk on, unmindful of the snow settling on my cap and coat, even on my beard, and see the visions of my mind rise up before me, as real as the spirals of the Kremlin churches. Vivid dreams. Of riding at the head of a Russian army into Kashmir. And then into Punjab. To the Harmandir at Amritsar. And finally into Lahore. Images of large crowds of my followers, my government around me, the Koh-i-noor back on my arm. Yes, I think I did seriously believe, then, that the prophecy would come true . . .

But despite these visions, it was a hopeless winter, cold and lonely, the winter after the coming of Pauline. The mood in Moscow had turned unhelpful and I could not make out friend from foe. It seemed as if all my plans were known even before they were made. I told Ada not to speak too much. To make matters worse, the Paris newspapers carried a terrible proclamation said to be jointly signed by me and the Afghan Jamal-ud-din. It called upon people to rise, it talked of plans underfoot to gain all support against the British, it promised that in due time, the real rulers of India would return, that war materials would be supplied, that several senior Europeans would join the rebellion. And another article appeared in New York linking me with the Irish revolutionaries in Paris. My name was being used by all manner of men and I was receiving the discredit. It would have been worth it if all this had actually brought me support for my plans against the British. It did not.

The Governor General of Moscow, Prince Dolgorouki, left me in no doubt of what the Russians thought: 'Your Highness, I must make it quite clear. Your connections with these unknown confederates are very disturbing, men like Jamal-ud-din and others whom I would rather not name.'

'Excellency, please believe me. I do not know this Jamal, though in all honesty I must admit I have heard his name, and that too only in Moscow.'

'You are said to have signed the proclamation, on behalf of some Indian Liberation Society, with him. Such secret societies are not permitted by the law in Russia.'

'I have not formed any society, Excellency, I have not even heard of it. I am here only to seek the assistance of His Imperial Majesty and you know that I am alone. I implore you to kindly assist me in seeking an audience with him. I have no doubt that he will see the truth of my case and the combined interest that we have in overthrowing the British in India.'

But there was not much hope; too much falsehood had been spread about me. And no doubt, the Czar's mind had been further poisoned against me by the Prince and Princess of Wales when they met him. The Czar probably did not realize my true worth in India but I daresay that the Prince of Wales did. So he must have done all he could to prevent the Russians from helping me. London was scared and I could not resist driving the point home. I wrote another proclamation addressed to the Sikhs that was published in America. Once again, I signed it as the Sovereign of the Sikh Nation, for that is who I am.

'*Sri Khalsa ji,*' I wrote, '*we exhort you to study the book of sakhians, the prophecies, wherein a glorious destiny is predicted, and to praise Sri Sat Guru ji in the holy temple of Amritsar in anticipation of deliverance . . . Hindoos, Muslims, Eurasians and native Christians, all creatures, like ourselves, of only one true fold, we love you all equally, beloved countrymen, in accordance with the tenets of Baba Nanak. Our quarrel is not with the inhabitants of Hindustan and not with our own race; it is with our hundred times accursed enemy, the British government . . .*'

My feelings were running high. I did indeed feel a true patriot, a proud implacable foe of England. It was as if after years of being in some drug-induced haze, I had come awake to light and life. At last, I knew who I was. I had so many dreams.

And I was part of so many tangled webs! I didn't know whom to trust. Everybody had his own iron in the fire . . . and how many cared for me and how much, I could never know. Today I know— I was alone then, and I am alone now. It disgusts me to think that not one nation, not one of the great European powers had the courage to dispel the wretched phantom of the British Crown; its false fear had spread deep and wide.

Arur Singh, winter 1893, Hardwar

It was a great pity that the Sandhawalia Sardar died so soon, just before I was arrested. There was much good work being done then. His agents were contacting our Sikh and Rajput brothers in the British cantonments. They were preparing them for my Maharaja's return, urging them to desert the British army, to indulge in mutiny and looting at the front and attack the British soldiery. There were elaborate plans to cut the telegraph and rail lines. Several soldiers from British regiments came to Thaker Singh. They would make the plea of going down to Rameshwaram temple but would leave the trains much before that and find their way to Pondicherry. There they would take the oath of allegiance, they would be told of our plans and they would then go back to their regiments and administer the oath to thousands. Even the Sikh soldiers in the Nizam's army were on our side. And the Kukas, they too began to look towards the Maharaja now that their Guru, Ram Singh, was no more, some even saying that their Guru's spirit had entered my Maharaja. The Sikh chiefs too—Nabha, Jind, Patiala—were committed.

All this was not a pipe dream though it may seem so now, now that my Maharaja is buried at Elveden. This is how revolutions are made, this is how empires are overturned. The British were shaken; I know it from the way they questioned me. If our plan had worked, Mangla Mai, your little child Duleep would have been King of Lahore again, and maybe of all India, and he would have ruled with gentleness and wisdom. We would have paid off the Russians for their efforts and sent them an annual tribute for helping us get rid of the British.

But we were betrayed at every stage. There were spies all over the place, around me, around the Maharaja. I am sure that Tevis was a spy and who knows if even that Ada was not? Our Maharaja talked too easily, loved too much. He was an emotional man, a man of the heart. And in the end, for reasons best known to them, the Russians didn't help him.

Duleep Singh, autumn 1893, Paris

The snow drifted down from the dark sky all night. It seemed to bring down a message from heaven: India is too far. Give it up, give up your dream. You are alone, you are trapped, you are spied upon all the time, you—King of Punjab—are poor. You are selling your dresses. Give up. Night after night the same feeling of despair. I was haunted by the faces of the people I would never reach.

And in the morning everything would be thick white. It would be difficult to even open the door of Hotel Billo and walk towards the road. Once in two or three days a man would shovel away enough for me to be able to step out. But mostly it lay thick where it fell—on the windowsills, on the bare branches outside that room, on the rooftops of the houses across the park.

Every door in Moscow seemed shut to me. There was no Katkov to raise my hopes, no E.C. to egg me on. Failure, like the snow, lay thick all around me. Dolgorouki told me that I must leave Moscow and I should give up all hope of an audience with the Czar. Russia did not want trouble with England; there was to be no war on the Afghan frontier. They had decided to be friends.

Even Hotel Billo began to seem expensive, so we moved to a private boarding house not far away from the Kremlin. It was much cheaper and it did not make Ada happy. There was just enough place for the two of us, the child and the dogs. Those days I slept with a pistol under my pillow.

My God! My God! Why could I not reach India?

Arur Singh, winter 1893, Hardwar

Jiwan Singh, who carried the letter you wrote, Mangla Mai, to my Maharaja in Aden was also picked up by the police, just like me. And he too was interrogated by that baboon-faced Henderson and his juniors. He cracked. He told them about the correspondence between the Sikhs in Pondicherry and the Maharaja and where all the letters were kept—and God knows how much else. Henderson was difficult to resist; he was a very cruel, a very clever man. And he knew every little detail there was to know about our plans. Only, I had decided that he would not get much from me.

As they arrested me, so they released me too. All of a sudden, on a morning in winter three years ago, I was asked to come out of my cell and was taken to the office of the Commandant.

'Arur Singh,' he said, 'there is good news today.'

'Is it good for you, sahib, or for me?'

'Good news for you. The Viceroy has shown his mercy. I have orders to release you from Chunar fort.'

I could not believe I had heard him right. I had by then lost all hope of being released ever, and I thought I would die in that cell, far away from everybody, never to see the Maharaja again.

'Yes, Arur Singh, you are free to go wherever you like, even to England. Here are your things.'

He then handed me over my leather pocket book . . . this one, I still carry it. In it was all the money there had been—my cheque for five hundred rupees, my four notes of hundred francs each from the French bank. As I walked out of the fort, a free man at last, I knew I would go back to my Maharaja.

Duleep Singh, autumn 1893, Paris

Tiflis, in Central Asia. That is where I wanted to go but Dolgorouki would have none of it. It was too near India. The Russians did not want to do anything that would look like they were using me against the British any longer. He suggested that I go in the other direction, to Kiev in the Ukraine. I accepted. I was desperate to leave Moscow.

It was a slow life, in the country house in Boyarka, just outside Kiev, among the wheat fields. But I thought it would be good for us to rest there, especially since Ada, weak after the child, did not keep well those days. Then we could always move, once the weather improved, to Algeria, or maybe the south of Italy. If I could not get my empire perhaps I could still get some good hunting in the Caucasus. My guns were once again with me, and on some days all I wanted was to be out in the open, watching the pheasants fly over my head, taking aim, feeling the gun recoil against my shoulder, smelling the barrel burning from the shot. That was a reality no one could take away from me; it brought me closest to being the great Ranjit's son.

But word about me had obviously travelled further than I knew. The Indian Prince, that's what they called me in Kiev. And many important men came to call on me, including the governor of the region ... I forget his name now ... And many noblemen. Many also listened to my case and offered to do all they could to get me assistance from the Czar. But nothing came of it.

Finally one day, more than a year after I had reached Russia with great hopes, I realized that it was all over. There was no point waiting on in Russia any more. The Czar was not going to meet me and there was nothing that could be done about it. I would be better off in Paris.

So I messaged Carrol-Tevis that I was returning on private business and quietly took the train to Odessa. Pauline was then ten months or so, a lovely little child, and my spaniels were still with me. A steamer took us from Odessa to Marseilles. After the monotonous months of the Russian plain with its endless snows and bare birch trees, the sight of water gave rest to the eyes. The Black Sea, the Bosphorus with its fabulous views of Constantinople, its mosques and minarets, and the blue of the Mediterranean were like a balm to me as I sat on the deck holding Pauline in my arms. Even Ada's spirits perked up; she made no secret of the fact that she was happy to leave behind the cold, the early dark evenings, the loneliness of Russia. Her face was a picture of joy when the steamer entered Marseilles harbour and her eyes rested on the spiral of Notre Dame de la Garde on the hill. I saw her giving her thanks to God.

General Carrol-Tevis, autumn 1893, Paris

When the lost Maharaja came back to his old group in Paris, he looked tired but not cured of his wild fancies. He hadn't quite realized despite the year of failure in Russia that he was not the centre of the world, that there were bigger games going on. But he had become less trusting, thinking that he would keep off the spies by moving houses frequently. Of course he still had no idea at all that his most trusted confidant was still in business. I listened.

'I intend not to give up, my friend,' he told me. 'I have still some cards up my sleeve. I will start auctioning my jewels—they can still fetch millions. Perhaps more than four million pounds. And with that I will raise and train an army to conquer not only Punjab but all India. I am even going to write to Her Majesty to restore the Koh-i-noor to me out of her privy purse.'

Because I knew him well by then—he was a wide open book, really—I wasn't struck dumb by the complete conviction with which he said this. Over several days he drove me insane with his elaborate plans for his fabulous Grand Army of Freedom!

'The weapons for my army will come from America. Casey has assured me that fifteen thousand Irishmen will revolt from within the British forces. There will be volunteers from Hungary, Austria, Russia, France . . . even Germany. They will fight for me without pay and when we reach India, there will be money enough to pay for all their services. There will be a fully organized army command—an army with generals, colonels, lieutenant colonels, majors. We will land in India and surprise the government. All of India will be ablaze.'

He had other plans too.

'I am now also the President of the League of Indian Patriots. This League will soon have followers in every town and village of India, all sworn to secrecy. Each member will contribute one anna a month towards arms and ammunitions. I am going to organize it all. There will be two Amirs in the League, one for the Sikhs and Hindus, another one for the Mohammedans.'

I began to pity him. The poor man was unhinged, I thought. Nevertheless I continued to do my duty to my masters and conveyed every conversation the same night to London.

Duleep Singh, autumn 1893, Paris

I had treated Ada as my wife, my Maharani, even before going to Russia, having married her according to Sikh rites. But that had not been enough to make little Pauline a legitimate child in the eyes of the French or the English. And even when Bamba was no more, it had not been possible for me to formally marry Ada, for by that time I had cut my ties with the British government and they would not have given me the certificates that I needed.

But ha, they did! Right there, in Paris, they delivered in my hand the certificate that my first wife was dead and I was a legitimate widower and a British subject, and my parents were dead, and I was free to marry whomsoever I liked.

I had a great laugh that day.

'Fooled them again!' I told Carrol-Tevis, waving the certificates triumphantly at him. 'First they gave me a passport in the name of Pat Casey and now they have given certificates to their sworn enemy! Some heads will roll and that's all to the good.'

But the Russians hauled me up. The minute the civil marriage was announced, they called me.

'Your documents were given to you on the basis of the declaration that the English lady with you was your wife,' the minister at the embassy told me. 'But clearly that was not a true declaration.'

'It was quite true. She is already my wife according to Sikh rites.'

But that did not cut much ice.

'We are changing the terms of your visa. You would no longer have the right to travel freely in Russia, should you return. You may stay in Finland or northern Russia, never in the Caucasus. And your baggage can only be allowed into Russia if you pay duty.'

I was angry and I was sad, but there was little I could do. The wedding had been announced, it would be gone through with. I wore my Star of India in my lapel, no one could stop me from doing that. And my Ada, my twenty-year-old bride, wore an unforgettable lavender wedding dress. All our close friends in Paris were there— E.C., Carrol-Tevis, and so many others. And when I had to sign the register, I did so with pride and flourish as 'Sovereign of the Sikh nation'. The mayor told the guests about my destiny and my deprivation, of my grand birth and the devilishness of the English.

That was four years ago, the summer of 1889 and Ada was already carrying Irene ...

I had thought that marriage may change Ada's wonder for grand and glamorous things, her spending habits. But that didn't happen. In fact the expenses increased as her mother and sister joined us in our apartment at Rue Marbeuf. All I had left was five thousand pounds. If the Russians had known that, they would have thought me a beggar and dropped me altogether. I began to sell my jewels, hoping to get at least four hundred thousand francs for them but that too was not to be. They sold for trifling amounts, the brooches and the necklaces. That necklace of perfect pearls, the one I wore when Victoria had me painted in Buckingham Palace, brought in only seven thousand francs.

There was no other source of money. Empty promises were all that I had from India, nice letters from Pondicherry, grand visions, but no money. And I could not move an inch without money. My Grand Army would remain a chimera.

General Carrol-Tevis, autumn 1893, Paris

I witnessed the marriage of this intense fool. I was the first to sign the register.

By then he was almost at the end of his rope. Nothing would have pleased him so much as a clear refusal of financial help from India, as that would have freed him from what he called his obligations to the sacred cause of his country's emancipation and allowed him to treat with England.

And he was running short of coin. His concubine was extravagant as only a chambermaid-turned-Maharani could have been. Her marriage to him lost him whatever support he had gathered in Russia. She was believed by them to be a paid English agent, so if he had married her, how could he be sincere to Russia? We had him truly encircled.

Duleep Singh, autumn 1893, Paris

Nothing from Kashmir, Hyderabad, Oudh, Pondicherry. Nothing from Russia. One by one the lights were going out, one by one the dreams vanished. India, Punjab, Lahore . . . all so far away.

And I was tired. Tired and alone. Wine was my only companion, morning and afternoon; wine stilled the pain in my heart, made me feel less small, wasted. That was the only way I could look out of the window and not believe that what I was seeing was the sunset of my own life. It was that drink that helped to kill the taste of defeat.

Sometimes Ada drank with me; at other times she sat and watched me drink, or left me to drink alone while she went out with her mother and sister or her friends so full of youth and desire that I began to wonder if it would not be kinder for me to set her free . . . I do not recall that she ever tried to hold me back from drink or say that I should drink less.

And how could she? She was just a young girl and I a king, even if a defeated king. I could do what I wanted. She needed money for shopping always … for food, for clothes, for entertainment. One way or the other I managed to give her the money, by selling jewels, selling my dresses. That was our compact. That way, I kept her chained to me.

General Carrol-Tevis, autumn 1893, Paris

The pretender was now, under the influence of his wife, fast becoming a besotted swine. His only endeavour was to get money out of the Indians to enable him to supply her every extravagance. She encouraged his wild drinking, taking him around the night houses in Paris. He was often too drunk to even sit straight in his carriage. His face was like that of a defeated prizefighter. And his people did not send him anything from India. They only wrote letters to thank me for the service I was performing for their 'beloved Sovereign'. If they had known the truth! Anyhow, the noose was tightening around them in Pondicherry; the French were not too keen to encourage Britain's enemies. Duleep Singh feared expulsion from Paris too. He was ready to sell out.

Duleep Singh, autumn 1893, Paris

That woman, Mrs Parraton, arrived from Russia and took over the entire household. I did not know who she was, or even if she was working for the Russians to spy on me. But Ada treated her as an old friend and when they both took a villa out of Paris for six months, I was pretty much left to my own devices.

So I moved to the Grand Hotel.

I have always liked the Grand, its majesty, its space, its huge lobby and its evergreen atrium. In the Grand I did not feel that I was a loser. I did not feel poor. It gave me a sense of hope, it assured me that there was still the possibility of a fight.

A small room was all that I could afford but better a small room in the Grand than a villa elsewhere. Sometimes, when I was too tired or when there had been too much drink, I would wish that the room were not so far away, that there were not quite so many steps to climb to get to it. Some people came calling on me, and no matter what the room, the address was still of the Grand Hotel, Paris. The Russian Notovich, who had been all over India, was one of those people. He had a notebook with names and photographs of the princes he had met in India and said several were sympathetic to me—Jaipur, Kashmir, the Nizam and Dholpur. He said that there was hope still. The Russians should support me, there should be rebellion in Punjab. And I, the chief Moghul of India, as he called me, would easily rule all of that land.

It was nice to hear him, it warmed me inside. It almost brought the fight back into my eyes. But when he had gone down those stairs, the doubts returned: was anyone listening at all?

Disaster struck soon after that. Suddenly I could not move. Not my hands, nor my legs, not even a finger. The darkness rose above my head, like the rising waters of some flood. Is this the way death comes? That was the only thought that ran again and again in my mind. I had no idea what was happening to me. Was my heart seizing on me or my brain? Somehow my eyes remained open. The light faded but did not fully vanish. I knew I had to find some help. With the one hand that I could move a bit, I pulled on a greatcoat over my shoulders and dragged my body down the steps towards the hotel lobby. I did not know whether it was morning or night until somehow I pushed myself out of the large glass doors and hailed a carriage. I could guide it to the doctor's house. The horse's hooves drummed holes in my head and with every turn of the street, the world went dark. It seemed to be the longest journey I had ever undertaken. The doctor was not at home. I struggled up to his porch and down, back to the waiting carriage. Another doctor, I told the coach driver, any doctor. We stumbled along the streets of Paris and ultimately I lay in the warm clinic of an unknown doctor.

'You have had a stroke, you need complete rest.'

They all gathered quickly about me then. Victor, Frederick and Ada, back from the villa. I needed them. I was helpless. I was paralysed. The Lion of Punjab too had had a stroke, and some had surmised from that that I was a bastard. How could a man felled by such a stroke sire a son, it was asked.

The doctor from the British embassy came to see me. 'It is a stroke, Your Highness,' he said. 'It can happen to anybody suffering from the ailments that you suffer from.'

Diabetes and Bright's disease are my ailments. Bright's disease had caused the high blood pressure that burst a vessel in my brain and left me a wreck. I lay between the three of them—Victor, Frederick, Ada—and the embassy doctor, convinced that I was going to die.

I heard Victor speak. 'How bad is it, doctor?'

'His Highness's left side is paralysed. Some movement may return, but I am afraid that recovery may be slow and unpredictable. I think the damage would have been less if he had not been alone when it happened, if he had not rushed about the city looking for a doctor.'

They moved me to a bigger, better room at the Grand for a while and then, when they thought I was a little better, away from the Grand altogether. It must have become expensive to go on staying there and a smaller hotel would do me no harm. Victor wanted to take charge of everything. I let him, though at times I wanted to exert myself.

But how does a man in my position, with one half of my face, my arm and leg paralysed, do anything? I waited for my friends to come and see me. And then I realized that Victor was picking who should and who should not meet me. All my friends, all who could qualify as enemies of Great Britain, were kept away.

'Father,' Victor spoke to me one of those evenings when I lay in the half darkness.

'Father, please listen to me. You are not well, in fact you are seriously sick. This is the time to seek a Royal pardon from Her Majesty.'

His words seemed to get to me with difficulty as if through thick London fog. A Royal pardon was what my son wanted me to plead for. He wanted me to give up the fight, to give up forever my claims, to give up the fight for justice, to give up what was his, to give up, finally, the throne of Lahore.

'That is the only way, Father. I promise you that you still have friends in England who will support you and I feel very strongly, in fact I *know* that Her Majesty will forgive you. You are weak and alone, Father. There is nobody who will help you in what you started, not Russia, not the princes of India. For your sake and for ours, please write to Her Majesty.'

I owed it to myself, he said; I owed it to them, my children, who hadn't chosen their position, this orphan, mongrel life—that is what he said one evening, in exasperation. I owed my blood this much— a Royal pardon and thus a kind of freedom for myself and for them.

At times I felt I could resist him; at other times, when all seemed lost, I wanted to agree with my child. Finally, one evening in that small hotel on the Champs Elysees I signed the letter that he dictated. I humbly asked Her Majesty to pardon me and I told her that I trusted entirely to her clemency. And if she granted me pardon, I promised her obedience for the future. My hand trembled so much that it was difficult to hold the pen. Truly, as was written in that letter, the hand of God had struck me down.

'I have been disappointed in everyone in whom I had been led to believe and now my one desire is to die at peace with all men. I therefore pray Your Majesty to pardon me for all I have done against you and your government and I throw myself entirely upon your clemency. It seems to me now that it is the will of God that I should suffer injustice at the hands of your people.'

God's will it was, else by then I would have succeeded and been crowned at the Golden Temple in Amritsar. It was as if in fighting against Great Britain I had been fighting against God. I had found no one to curse Great Britain. God himself, it seemed, had blessed her, despite all her faults and injustices.

Victor wrote other letters, even that letter to my supporters in Pondicherry. He told them, saying that it was my opinion, that they should all seek clemency from the Queen, that the struggle had been abandoned. Destroy all letters of the Maharaja, do not let yourself be compromised, he wrote. The Maharaja has submitted and retired from all political activity, he told them. Find the best course for yourself.

It was done. I had surrendered. But I refused to agree to live in England. It would be too painful. I had travelled too far down the road of rebellion.

When my old friend Ronald Leslie-Melville came to see me, I cried like a child, helplessly, in his arms.

'The Almighty has felled me, Ronald. It is my just deserts for the horrible way in which I have behaved towards Her Majesty. You know better than anyone else how she used to care for me. Where are those days, those years gone? Why did all her officials, those petty officials, not realize how she cared for me and what regard I held her in? If only they had, things would never have come to such a pass . . . I have written to her, Ronald, I have sought her pardon. I hope she can find the kindness to forgive me. I could once again find all my old friends. Friends like you, Ronald, and like Grafton and Henniker. All of you understand what I truly am. I want to die at peace with everyone. I want to be forgiven by everyone.'

I did not care what I said then, in what manner, and I do not care now . . . It was over, everything.

Victor did his bit to further clarify matters. I would be loyal, he told them, absolutely loyal. There would be no more wild plotting.

The India Office must have been overjoyed to receive that letter. I could imagine their smug expressions when they read it. Is that all, they must have thought, that there was to it? What happened to the plans, the proclamations, the prophecy? What happened to the grand plans of a Russian invasion?

The Secretary of State wrote that Her Majesty had granted the pardon, provided that henceforth I would remain obedient to her and would regulate my movements in accordance with instructions received. Again the regulation of my movements . . . A prisoner till the end.

The letter was read out to me; I was in no shape to sit up and read it myself. Let them regulate all my movements. I could hardly move even in my bed. I had rebelled against England and now once again, all around me were Englishmen. Doctors, friends . . . even my sons behaving like Englishmen. All others were kept at bay.

Aur Singh, winter 1893, Hardwar

I did not go back to my Maharaja empty-handed. A full five thousand pounds was collected and sent to the Pondicherry banker and I took the list of the thirty generous souls who had contributed back to the Maharaja. But there too we met deceit. The money was never delivered to the Maharaja in Paris. It was not my fault, Mangla Mai.

In any case by then the Maharaja was a cripple, hobbling his way slowly on the beaches of southern France where Ada and Victor took him. They would be gambling away—*his* money of course—in the Casino and he spent his days locked up in a hotel room, unable to even turn his side without my assistance. Only in the evenings would we walk slowly along the water's edge. Mostly he would be quiet and sad and once in a while I would see a tear escape his eye. He would look out towards the sea and sit down on the benches that were spread along the beach and often I would sit with him and watch the sun set into the water.

What a beautiful sight that is, Mangla Mai. Those of us who have never seen the sea cannot imagine the beauty of that moment when the day comes to an end and the sun goes to rest for the night.

On other evenings he would fulminate and vent his anger and then sit down on some bench, drained and tired. He would curse his destiny, he would curse the British officials who had done him in, right from Dalhousie down, and he would curse the Russians. He would say things about Ada, and even about his sons that he would never have said in front of them.

'Treachery, all around, Arur, my son, treachery all around. They have made me seek the pardon that I did not want . . . and they still do not recompense me in any way. Never believe these people; I should have known better than to believe in anyone. It all came to nought because I did.'

That Ada. Not a care did she have for his condition, not a care for the trouble he was having with money. And her sister and mother were like vultures, picking at every piece of jewellery they could get their hands on, telling her to get more and more from my Maharaja. Once when I went with him to see that old French friend E.C., I heard him say—'I am poisoned! I am a dead man!' E.C. was alarmed and looked at the Maharaja as if all his troubles had affected his mind. But who knows—that Ada and her Russian friend could indeed have been poisoning the Maharaja slowly. He was drinking very hard too and she let him. At times, he seemed to be so troubled that even I thought that everything within him was breaking up. His heart sought revenge all the time and once, when young Oliphant, the man who was taking care of the children in England, was with him, I heard him raise his hands to the sky and say:

'Oh God, come to my assistance. Help me crush my enemies.'

Yes, he was a very desperate man by then. A man can only do that much, and he had done as much as his circumstances would allow him. And so did all of us, his foot-soldiers. But by then, there was little hope from any direction and no money. He couldn't even do the things that he had done all his life and liked so much, things like shooting and hunting. I thought of the Elveden days, of the endless top-class shooting parties. But then nothing stays forever.

On some days I used to think it would take very little for him to go back to England, a broken, tired poor man. On such days, I would sit at his knee, hold his hand, and pray with him for better days.

And then something would happen to raise his hopes again and for a few days the visions of our return to India would once again lighten his mood, make him get up in the morning and hobble out in enthusiastic style, write letters, have meetings and so on. Like the time that ugly Abdul Rasul came back. They hugged each other and became friends again. The Maharaja once again wrote through him to the Raja of Kashmir and to others and for a while they plotted with Zobair Pasha . . . The idea was a huge rising against the British in Egypt at the same time as the rising in India.

That was never to be, like so many other things. His health was failing fast . . . half paralysed, they say his kidneys began to shut down. He would lie all day in bed silently, alone. There was one important day for him, when he was taken to meet Queen Victoria, who happened to be nearby. In that French town on the hill above the sea—I forget the name of the place now. But I know that he could not restrain himself when he saw her. He wept and begged for her pardon and she forgave him.

Victor took him away to England after that, along with Ada and the girls. He did it quietly, so that none of the Maharaja's friends would know. But I knew it when they were arguing about the payment for the tickets.

'Let them pay for me to go, Victor, if they want me to go back to England.'

'I shall write, Father, but they may not agree.'

'Tell them I have no money. All my money is now in Russia. Let them pay for my tickets. After all, they paid for me when I left for India, only to be halted at Aden. Also, seek an advance for our expenses in England. Remember always, they owe me, owe you, a lot. They owe us a kingdom.'

Of course they paid for the tickets and I think they even sent some more money for the expenses of the family. For me it was a sad moment. My Maharaja was going back a tired and very sick man . . . and four years earlier he had started with such hopes on the *Verona*.

Duleep Singh, autumn 1893, Paris

It was strange to see the coast of England again after four years. So much had happened in those four years of intrigue, hope, despair and surrender. Even my body was only half mine. And there once again stood the cliffs of Dover.

Somehow I did not feel that I was coming home.

But I was delighted to see the children. Freddie, Sophia and Edward came first, and then to my joy, Bamba and Catherine came back from Germany. The two had grown into beautiful young women. As I embraced them, some of the gloom in my heart lifted, and there was a strange, comforting defiance. My children were people of courage: Nothing had been their fault, while it was possible that some may have been mine, and they wouldn't let the great games of fate and empires rob them of the will to live as they wished. We had been made pawns, all of us, but our triumph lay in refusing to play the game. We would upset the script, find our own unruly lives to lead. I spent some time with my children at Folkestone and then, inevitably, Ada and I returned to Paris.

One day in Paris, not so long ago, I went to meet E.C. I cannot remember when it was—last month, maybe last year. I forget these things now . . . and somehow it doesn't seem to matter. I reached him with difficulty, for then, as now, I walk only with considerable effort, and speak with even more.

'I must tell you, my dear doctor,' I told him, 'why I have changed my mind and signed my surrender and abdication—for that is what it is. So that all who have been compromised in my cause are given full pardon and so that my marriage with Ada is recognized as legal and the pension restored to my children. I have little time to live, I can see that, but I wanted to get as much back for my children as I could. That is the best that I could do. But there are times I regret what I have done.'

I try not to slip into self-pity. Kings, even deposed kings, should not indulge in self-pity. They should fight. But the fight does not seem worth it.

I wish for happier times, I wish for health, strength and vision. I want to be out shooting pheasants again, I want to feel the heather against my thighs and smell the gunpowder in the early morning freshness. I want to see my sons around me, walking with me, looking up to me. I want to be with Bamba, I want to apologize to her, I want to put my head in her lap and cry.

And I want, always, to see the smiles of my daughters, Catherine and Bamba, and the two young ones who hardly know me.

And what is there to pity myself about in any case? I could have held on to what I had in England. But I had made my decisions. I decided to take on the Crown, I decided to go to India, I left Bamba and I took Ada . . . All this I did. All this I need not have done . . . Then why pity myself?

Arur Singh, winter 1893, Hardwar

He went to England once again, to see his young son who lay dying of pneumonia. That broke his heart—to see his thirteen-year-old waiting to be taken into the arms of God. He could not wait there till the end. Nor was he well enough to go when they buried the boy next to his mother in the Elveden churchyard. But that day he lay in his bed, silent, sobbing, lost, looking towards the wall as if all the answers to the great riddles of life were written there.

After that I think he lost the will to live. In the early days of that month, that month of October, he called me to his bed. He called me his son, his only son because I was always with him when he needed me. And then he gave me two envelopes that I should deliver personally, he said, to Prince Victor and Ada after his death, which he said was near. 'And remember, Arur,' he added, 'I have already written in my will that I should be buried wherever I die, and it seems that it shall be here, in Paris. Keep my funeral as simple, as inexpensive as possible.'

I know what is on your mind, Mangla Mai, I know. Why did he say buried? He should have said cremated, like a Sikh. I think these things no longer mattered to him, if they ever did. He had become a Sikh again, it is true. But it was more an act of rebellion, and also a way of connecting with Punjab, with his people, and finding, for once, a home. Remember, he had lived virtually his whole life as a Christian, away from his own people.

Duleep Singh, autumn 1893, Paris

I cannot think clearly now. Darkness all around and a silence that I try to shatter with all my strength. I try to shriek but I am unable to. Why is everything so dark? Where is everybody? I know that there is nobody here. Ada went away somewhere, somewhere in England. I think Freddie went with her. Something about a smaller house, they said. For whom? Maybe for me. But why? I don't want to live in England any more. I have told them that so many times but they don't listen to me. Nobody listens to me any more. Maybe because I am old. But I am not old. I have seen men so much older than me. Maybe because I am poor and sick and dying. Finally dying. Victor too is not here. He too has gone somewhere. The little girls are with me. They come to see me. Their nanny brings them to see me. They came this morning. Is it not morning any more? The hands of that clock do not move. I cannot make out which is the hour hand. And I cannot make out anything beyond the window.

Is that a sunrise or a sunset . . . how does it matter? But the girls came, maybe today, maybe yesterday. Such pretty little girls. My two youngest daughters. My little Pauline and little Irene. Such a little child. She will not even remember me if I die now. I am dying now. I know it. She will remember me even if she does not remember me. That's because I have given her, in fact I have given them both, the hawk's bells. The little bells that once my falcons wore. Oh those falcons. Oh those days in Fattehgarh . . . Shivdeo running after me. Always running after me . . . wanting to do all the things that I did. Always trying to be me. But he did not come with me to England. He wanted to. His mother did not let him . . . So many men . . . no names that I recall but some faces are like those of old friends looking after me, taking care of me . . . and the falcons hunting and circling in the blue sky over the huge old trees and coming back and sitting on the back of my hand . . . with those bells on their toes. And the mosquitoes of Fattehgarh, those huge black clouds that used to rise from the river. Those whirlwinds of mosquitoes were evil spirits, the servants used to say. Do not get under those mosquitoes, Maharaja, evil spirits reside in them . . . they will get into your body. And I would laugh. I want to laugh now. I cannot even laugh now . . . How I used to laugh . . .

The bells are with my little girls now. They took the bells and went away.

'I am writing to my mother.' I think it was Pauline who said that. I told her to do something . . . Maybe I told her to send my love to her mother. That's what I always say. Always sending her my love. That's why I married her, because I love her. So I sent Ada my love. Pauline will send her my love. There is nobody in the room now, I think, there is nobody at the door. I think it is only the wind against the window. I want to sleep . . . sleep for a very long time . . . but the door is shut. Like they shut the gate of the fort behind me, and I felt I was safe. But my uncle was dead . . . there was blood all over and my mother shrieked and wailed. But when the gate was shut, I was safe. I am safe now. Abdul Rasul cannot shoot me . . . he once aimed his pistol at me. And all the Englishmen are scared of me . . . they are scared that if I enter Punjab, it will be all over for them. The Punjabi soldiers will support me, always . . .

But Sandhawalia misled me. Made me give up everything that I had in England. I became a Sikh again. I took the pahul in Aden. I hated Aden. So hot and muggy, and never again did I see Bamba. I disowned her—I had found Ada . . . These tears that flow now are all for you, dearest Bamba. I have seen this kind of darkness before . . . when was it. I cannot remember dates and years any more . . . It was the time of smallpox, that much I remember. And through this kind of darkness I saw only a flickering flame, and sometimes, faintly, my mother's face. I search again in this darkness. I cannot see any flame. I cannot even see Bibiji's face. I wish I could sit with her, put my head in her lap. Maybe then this pain would still, maybe the darkness would lift. The elephants are running . . . and I am laughing. Elephants with silver howdahs . . . mine had a brilliant red carpet in the howdah. My elephant is again ahead of Shivdeo's, always ahead . . . And why is this pain rising again in my chest? I thought it had gone, gone forever. And the swirl of mosquitoes over my head. And there is someone at the door . . . No, no it is only the wind . . . At least I gave away the hawk's bells to the girls. They will remember me that way, they will remember me as someone who gave them those bells . . . It is all right to die.

Arur Singh, winter 1893, Hardwar

Alone, Mangla Mai, so alone. In a room in a small cheap hotel in a narrow street in Paris. The King of Lahore! He died alone. Even this unfortunate soul was not there to hold his hand, give him water, shut his eyes the day the Waheguru called him home. We all reached too late.

The British embassy was told. They told Queen Victoria. She sent a telegram to Victor. He read it out to everybody who had by then gathered in Paris—Ada, Freddie . . . She remembered how handsome and charming the Maharaja had been in the early years when he used to spend a lot of time with her. She said that the later years had been painful for her but at least they had met and had made up in that French town—the name I still cannot get.

Telegrams, flowers, wreaths—they kept pouring in, but what use are these to a dead man? Would he not have exchanged all those good wishes for the presence of one person at his bedside when he breathed his last?

We took him by boat across the Channel. Of course nobody listened when I said that he had wanted to be buried where he had died. He had told me that. He had written it down. Victor said that he would be buried in Elveden next to Maharani Bamba and that was that. By boat across the waters and then by a train to Thetford. In a way, I think it was good. At least he was where people knew him, near people who had seen him as a lord of the estate. The farmers and gamekeepers, the people who lived on Elveden loved him. He had always been kind to them.

All night he lay in his coffin in the church and in the morning the people came from London. The three girls, his dear daughters, looking so sad behind their black veils and men from the government, different men representing the Queen, the Prince of Wales, the Secretary of State.

It was all very simple, just the way he had wanted it. He was carried to his grave by the men who had worked for him—the head gardener, the head woodsman, the head gamekeeper and the other keepers. Men with whom he had spent years in the estate, walking around, shooting, joking. They all came to say farewell to their Black Prince.

Mangla, winter 1893, Hardwar

My heart is heavy, Arur, heavy with your story, with Duleep's pain. I no longer care if these tired old eyes see another sunrise or not. I too now wish to join them all in the heavens. I want to go and serve them again, my beautiful Maharani Jindan, my little, innocent Duleep. To be robbed of a home outside and within—in the heart! They put a wilderness inside him. The thought of his loneliness makes my heart tremble, and he lived it, Arur, every day of his life. Waheguru will grant you heaven for staying with him till the end.

Let me rest, Arur, and you rest too—you have endured more than us all. And let us pray that some day our Duleep's ashes will be brought home and scattered on the five rivers of Punjab. That is where he belongs, that is where he yearned to be. Close to his people, close to his mother. If that happens, then all of us who have been part of his story, people like you and me, can also die in peace.

EPILOGUE

But there he lies, in a grave, beside his Maharani and his son, in a cold wet land, far away from his people. Sometimes there is a flower on his grave, or even a fading bouquet. But mostly there are only brown fallen leaves that rustle in the wind.

And his memory will fade. His eight daughters and sons too are gone and not one of them left an heir. Perhaps this too was written. Or perhaps there was an imperial design. After all, it is known that Queen Victoria ordered the wife of Victor never to have children. Perhaps our Punjab was to be left only with the memory of a Maharaja-in-exile. Only with a story to be told around winter bonfires.